Editorial

This issue of *Warship* ranges perhaps further than any of its predecessors, going back to the Battle of Tsushima in 1904.

Tsushima ranks second only to Jutland as the most significant and intriguing fleet action of modern times. It is, of course, one of the great decisive battles of history, but much more than that, it is a clash of rival philosophies. In a sense it was not an example of Russian *materiel* against Japanese, but the French ideas of ship-design, which had been the most recent influence over the Imperial Russian Navy, against the largely British-inspired and British-built Japanese fleet. Paradoxically, the British/Japanese system was not subjected to anything like as severe a test as the French/Russian system.

One of the puzzling points about Tsushima is how so little was learned, given the comprehensive reports which were filed by British officers and technical advisers. The full reports were not even translated from the Japanese until 1917, a year after Jutland revealed so many weaknesses in damage control. The reason is easy to guess at: the pace of technical advance was so rapid that technical officers felt that a battle involving pre-dreadnought battleships could have no relevance when the Royal Navy was building 25 000-ton super-dreadnoughts. Perhaps there is a lesson in this for

today's naval planners, who seem often to assume that 'it will never happen again'.

Norman Friedman's discussion of the first American cruisers built within the limits of the Washington Treaty brings to light something new. It has always been held that the 10 000-ton, 8inch gun limits were either arbitrarily chosen or influenced by the existence of the British *Hawkins* class, with their 7.5inch guns. However the evidence shows quite clearly that the Bureau of Construction and Repair had already drawn up several designs of similar size with 8inch guns. This in turn points to an interesting contrast: the British delegation at Washington, with a clear idea of the sort of battleship they wanted, and the Americans fighting for the sort of cruiser they needed.

Our pictorial feature is contributed by Lawrence Sowinski, and covers the alterations and additions to the famous *Essex* class fleet carriers. As the most famous and most successful carriers ever built they ought to be better known than they are, but being turned out in such large numbers meant that to the inexperienced eye, one *Essex* looks much like another. The legendary efficiency of US repair yards also meant that ships acquired new gear very rapidly and were often radically changed in quite short overhauls. What Lawrence

Sowinski has done is to show the system behind the changes. It is all too easy to compile lists of armaments and modifications, but what is much more use to technical historians, modellers and photograph-collectors is to trace the process and thereby explain *why* and in what order the changes occurred.

The first in our series of ships never built is Alan Raven's drawing of a proposed 7-turret *Colony* class cruiser. The design files show that among others, a design existed for a *Fuji* class cruiser with seven twin 5.25inch guns in place of the four triple 6inch later chosen. These sketch-designs are among the most fascinating items in any design history, but it must always be remembered that they are never anything more than preliminary sketches. The detailed design stage usually sees the less practicable features eliminated, as constructors get down to the job of fitting everything in. Ships are logical creations, just like buildings, and one of the greatest virtues of model-making is that it often shows the intelligent modeller just why a warship finishes up the way she does. A feature that looks odd is often the only way in which certain arrangements can be accommodated without sacrificing other equally desirable features.

Antony Preston

The Design and Construction of

Between 1906 and 1914 ten battlecruisers were constructed for the Royal Navy. These ships can be roughly divided into two design groups. The first group, the six ships of the *Invincible* and *Indefatigable* classes, armed with 12inch guns were virtually big-gun armoured cruisers. The second group, the *Lion, Princess Royal, Queen Mary* and *Tiger,* armed with 13.5inch guns, being larger, faster and slightly better-protected, conformed more closely to the term battlecruiser.[1] They were too powerful to be described as armoured cruisers and insufficiently protected to be classed as fast battleships and this 'falling between two stools' just about sums up the battlecruiser concept. Apart from the major design change between the first and second group, improvements between successive classes were comparatively few.

This was mainly caused by the necessity to produce new designs and lay down new ships yearly to meet the demands of the naval race then in progress with Germany.

Designs generally were based on the design of the previous year's programme, with such modifications as necessitated by new technical developments and any new ideas that occured to the personnel involved in the design procedure. This process was largely undertaken on paper without the benefit of sea trials and sea experience with recent designs. For example, in 1911 when the *Tiger,* the last of the second group, was being designed the three ships of the *Invincible* class and the *Indefatigable* were the only battlecruisers completed and in service. It is also worth noting that the battlecruiser designs were developed in parallel with

contemporary battleship designs and new features in the latter were generally adopted in the former. Thus when the 13.5inch gun was introduced and fitted in the *Orion* class battleships the *Lion* class of the same year's programme was designed to employ the same weapon. Similar comments apply to superstructure and rig layout, secondary armament, searchlights, armour distribution (but not thickness) and so on. In this respect the *Tiger,* which was the last ship of pre-war battlecruiser type, gained more from the *Iron Duke* class battleships of the same year's programme than she did from the *Queen Mary* on which her design was based.

1911 — THE FIRST DESIGNS
The programme for 1911-12 made provision for the construction of four battleships and one

[1] All these vessels were originally classified as armoured cruisers until the term 'battlecruiser' was officially adopted in 1913.

the Battlecruiser

TIGER

by John A Roberts

The *Tiger* in September 1928.
Wright & Logan

battlecruiser. The design of the battleships, the *Iron Duke* class, was worked out during the first half of 1911, two main improvements being adopted in the design: an increase in the calibre of the secondary armament guns from 4inch to 6inch to counter the latest types of torpedo craft, and an after torpedo flat providing an additional underwater torpedo tube on each beam. The inclusion of these features in the battlecruiser design was a logical step and this was proposed by the Controller (Third Sea Lord), Rear Admiral C J Briggs, in a memo accompanying three preliminary sketch designs submitted to the Sea Lords in August 1911.[2] The details of these designs with those of the *Queen Mary* are given in Table 1.

Design 'C' was generally similar to *Queen Mary* but owing to the re-positioning of bulkheads necessitated by the provision of an after torpedo flat, it was found convenient to place the after funnel and main mast forward of 'Q' turret. In designs 'A' and 'A1' the turrets were arranged two forward and two aft and a 6inch gun secondary battery was provided. This latter involved an increase in topweight and in order to maintain the level of stability the beam was increased to 90 ft. As the armour protection for the 6inch battery was somewhat better than that for the 4inch battery this modification also

had the effect of improving the ship's protection by adding 8½ ft to the height of the side armour. The belt was further improved by the addition of a strip of armour 3 in thick and 2 ft 6 in deep below the main belt. This, the DNC explained, was regarded with great importance by the Japanese who were fitting similar protection in vessels then under construction in Japan and in the battlecruiser *Kongo* then being constructed by Vickers at Barrow. The Covers give no clue as to the reason for this Japanese innovation, apart from the fact that it was as a result of experience in the Russo-Japanese War. It does seem likely, however, that it was designed to defeat diving shell, or to prevent shells getting under the belt in a heavy swell, or both.

It is worth mentioning here that this is the only evidence in the Ship's Covers of any connection between the designs of *Tiger* and *Kongo*. Claims that the design of *Tiger* was heavily influenced by that of the Japanese ship seem to have been based on the similarity in appearance and the adoption of the same heavy secondary battery whereas, as can be seen from the above, these features resulted from entirely different considerations completely unconnected with the *Kongo*.

The Sea Lords agreed with the Controller's submission regarding

the secondary and torpedo armament and expressed a preference for design 'A1'. But the arcs of fire of the secondary armament were criticised as being restricted, particularly fore and aft. It was suggested that these be improved and, to further improve the general command of the battery, that a 6inch gun be placed on each side of the forecastle deck in the positions occupied by the 12pdr guns in design 'A'. A preference was expressed for the disposition of main armament in design 'C' because 'the two (aft) turrets (in designs 'A' and 'A1') practically form one target when, with sufficient separation, as in 'C', it means the enemy has three separate targets to fire at which complicates his fire control. This is important up to 10 000 yards'. This statement shows a somewhat dated view of naval gunnery; the days when one part of a ship could be aimed at were rapidly fading. However, the argument had some

Design A (top) with 6inch gun secondary battery and C (bottom) with 4inch gun secondary battery. Design A1 was much the same as A but did not have the 12pdr guns on the forecastle deck abreast the bridge. The above drawings are based on the verbal descriptions of the designs in the 'Ships Cover' — the actual sketches not being present. The distribution of the secondary battery is assumed, apart from being on the correct deck.

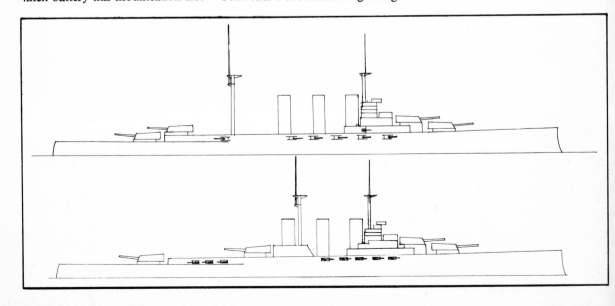

TABLE 1 — **LEGEND OF DESIGNS JULY 1911**

	A	A1	C	Queen Mary
LENGTH (PP)	660ft	660ft	660ft	660ft
BEAM	90ft	90ft	89ft	89ft
LOAD DRAUGHT	28ft 6in	28ft 3in	28ft 3in	28ft
DEEP DRAUGHT	32ft 6in	32ft 3in	32ft 3in	32ft 1in
DISPLACEMENT	28450 tons	28100 tons	27250 tons	27000 tons
TPI	101	101	99	99
SHP	80000	79000	76000	75000
SPEED	28 knots			
FUEL AT LOAD DRAUGHT	1000 tons			
COAL CAPACITY	3700 tons			
OIL FUEL CAPACITY	1100 Tons			
COMPLEMENT	1000 (Queen Mary 999)			

ARMAMENT
8—13.5inch/45 cal (80 rpg)
12—6inch/45 cal (150 rpg) A and A1 C and *Queen Mary*
16—4inch/50 cal (150 rpg)
2—1/ pdr (250 r pg) *in A only*
5—Maxim machine guns (5000 rpg)
4—(6 in A1) 3 pdr saluting guns
4—21inch torpedo tubes (2 in *Queen Mary*)
20—21inch torpedoes (14 in   ,,   )
6—14inch torpedoes (for 50ft steam boats)

ARMOUR
MAIN BELT	9, 5 and 4inch
UPPER BELT	6, 5 and 4inch
LOWER BELT	3inch (Not in *Queen Mary* and C)
SECONDARY BATTERY	5inch (A and A1) 3inch (*Queen Mary* and C)
BULKHEADS	4inch
BARBETTES	9 and 8inch
GUNHOUSES	inch
CONNING TOWER	10inch
CONTROL TOWER (AFT)	6inch

PROTECTIVE PLATING
WING BULKHEADS TO
MAGAZINE AND SHELL
ROOMS	1½ and 1inch
FUNNEL UPTAKES	1½ and 1inch
DECKS	1inch to 3inch (1inch to 2½inch in *Queen Mary* and C)

WEIGHTS (TONS)

	A	A1	C	Queen Mary
GENERAL EQUIPMENT	820	820	820	805
ARMAMENT	3,860	3,650	3,450	3,352
MACHINERY	5,780	5,720	5,500	5,460
COAL	1,000	1,000	1,000	1,000
ARMOUR & PROTECTIVE				
PLATING	7,030	6,980	6,730	6,595
HULL	9,860	9,830	9,6500	9,760
BOARD MARGIN	100	100	100	28
TOTAL	28,450	28,100	27,250	27,000
ESTIMATED COST	£2,235,000	£2,199,000	£2,100,000	£2,085,000

[2]Memo (dated 31 July 1911) and designs were examined initially by First Sea Lord, Admiral Sir A K Wilson, and were then passed on to the Second and Fourth Sea Lords, Vice-Admiral Sir G Le C Egerton and Captain Charles E Madden respectively.

validity in that with the turrets well apart the chances of a single heavy shell or torpedo immobilising both turrets was remote. A few other minor criticisms were made, including the statement that only one mast was required as a second was unnecessary.

To meet these criticisms the First Sea Lord gave verbal instruction for a new sketch design based on 'A1' but incorporating the following modifications:—

a Main armament disposed as in design 'C'.

b Forward 6inch gun embrasures altered to give an arc of fire of 3° across bow.

c An added 6inch gun casemate on each side of the forecastle deck.

On 14 August the new design, designated 'A2', was submitted by the DNC, Sir Phillip Watts, and four days later received Board approval. Criticism was limited to a further request for improvements in the arcs of training of the 6inch guns. The DNC estimated that the 6inch gun casemates would involve an additional weight of 90 tons but the legend of 'A2' was identical to that of 'A1'. However, more detailed calculation of the design resulted in a number of alterations to the legend and on 12 November this document provided the figures shown in Table 2. Under normal circumstances this would have been the end of the basic design stage, but events were developing which were to bring further improvement to the *Tiger*.

1911-12 — THE NEW BOARD
For some time important sections of Parliament, the Press and the Navy had been campaigning for the formation of a Naval War Staff. The attitude of the Admiralty to

this idea was to say the least luke-warm. The Agadir crisis of July 1911 brought matters to a head and resulted in the Secretary of State for War, R B Haldane, pressing the Prime Minister for a change at the Admiralty. As a result, on October 25 the Home Secretary, Winston Churchill, exchanged posts with the First Lord, Reginald McKenna. Churchill entered the Admiralty with two main objectives, the formation of a Naval Staff and the appointment of Board of Admiralty of his own choosing. He did not take long; the former took place in January 1912 and the latter was announced in Parliament on 28 November 1911. Admiral Wilson, the First Sea Lord, who was completely opposed to a Naval Staff, was replaced by Admiral Sir Francis Bridgeman and the posts of Second and Fourth Sea Lords were taken by Vice-Admiral Prince Louis

of Battenberg and Captain W Pakenham respectively. Admiral Briggs, as Controller and Third Sea Lord, was the only member of the original Board to remain. The new Board took up its duties on 5 December.

One of Churchill's first acts upon hearing of his new appointment was to seek the advice of Admiral Sir John Fisher (First Sea Lord 1905-1910). The two spent three days of discussion together in Reigate Priory and Fisher was 'most of all . . stimulating in all matters related to the design of ships'[3]. Churchill was strongly influenced by the old Admiral's dynamic personality and later events show that he took up several of Fisher's favourite themes. Among these were the desire for ships of high speed and a belief in the advantages of oil fuel over those of coal. Churchill's habit of becoming more involved than was

[3] *The World Crisis, 1911-1918*, Winston Churchill

A rare photograph of *Tiger* in 1915 near the Forth Bridge. The 'TI' on 'Q' and 'A' turrets obviously indicates *Tiger* but the purpose of the triangle on the side of Y turret is not known. The bottom section of the lowered fore topmast can be seen between the legs of the tripod foremast. Note the incomplete sternwalk and the 24inch searchlight on the roof of 'Q' turret, transferred from its normal starboard position on the platform abaft the third funnel.
Imperial War Museum

usual for a Civil Lord soon became apparent. On 20 November he penned the following memo: 'I am making enquiries into the design of this (armoured) cruiser (*Tiger*) which will not be complete for a few days. After this tenders may be invited'.

On 12 December the detailed design and legend of 'A2' was submitted to the Board and approved 'subject to certain modifications to secure additional SHP' — a requirement obviously instigated by Churchill. It was also decided that tenders could be invited but that action regarding the placing of the order would be considered by the Board at a later date. Immediately after this meeting Churchill sent a memo to the Controller asking if the machinery of the *Iron Duke* class and *Tiger* could be adapted to run on oil fuel only. Three days later the DNC

TABLE 2 LEGEND OF DESIGN A2. NOVEMBER 12, 1911

Particulars as those for A1 except as follows:—

BEAM	90ft 6in
DISPLACEMENT	28,200 tons
SHP	82,000
COAL CAPACITY	3,750 tons
OIL CAPACITY	1,150
6 INCH AMMUNITION	200 rpg
CREW	1,109

WEIGHTS	
GENERAL EQUIPMENT	840 tons
ARMAMENT	3,600 tons
MACHINERY	5,500 tons
COAL	1,000 tons
ARMOUR & PROTECTIVE PLATING	7,390 tons
HULL	9,720 tons
BOARD MARGIN	100 tons
	28,200 tons

Note: There were also changes to armour arrangement and thicknesses including increasing the secondary battery armour to 6inch thickness.

Tiger as designed, 1911. Bridge and
funnels not yet raised; pole foremast; twin
24 inch searchlights on forward shelter
deck, abreast fore funnel and abreast
torpedo C.T. abaft 3rd funnel; range
finder on roof of torpedo C.T.; boats on
forecastle deck protected by blast screen
from fire of 'Q' turret. Top of masts are
not shown in design drawings and
arrangement is assumed.

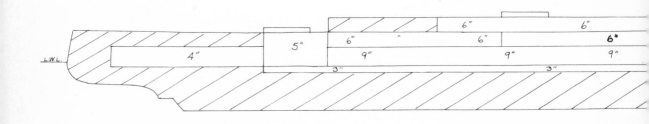

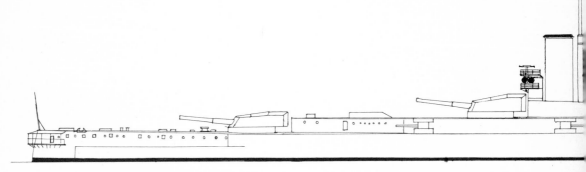

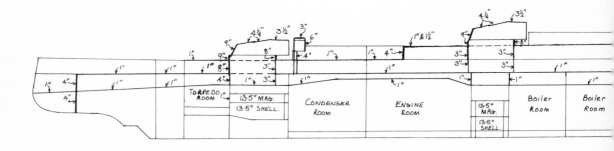

Longitudinal section showing armour
thicknesses (bottom) and hull profile
showing distribution of side armour (top);
shaded area is unprotected.

sent to the Controller two new
sketch designs, 'A2a' and 'A2b',
based on design 'A2'. In 'A2a' the
SHP was increased to 100 000 for a
speed of 29.5 knots which required
an additional 100 tons for
machinery, increasing the
displacement to 28 300 tons and the
draught to 28 ft 4 in. In 'A2b' the
SHP was further increased to 108
000 giving a speed of 30 knots,
adding 350 tons to the machinery

weight and 50 tons to the hull
weight. In addition the fuel capacity
was modified to 2450 tons coal and
2450 tons oil fuel, 450 tons of each
being allowed for at load draught.
This gave a legend displacement of
28 500 tons at a draught of 28 ft 6
in. In answer to Churchill's inquiry
the DNC commented that the
modifications necessary for all-oil
fuel stowage would present no
difficulty, but that to carry the

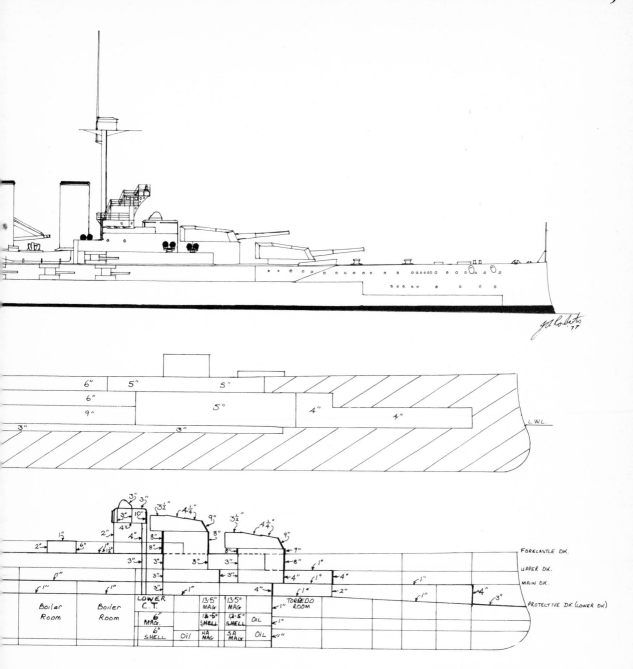

same total amount would require some oil to be carried above the protective deck, which was undesirable. He also pointed out that the loss of protection provided by the coal above this deck would be considerable. The Controller, in submitting the DNC's legends and comments to the Board, expressed a preference for design 'A2b' which would while 'increasing speed and stowage of oil give valuable

experience during construction'. Churchill, and presumably the rest of the Board, approved design 'A2b' on 19 December. Two days later invitations to tender were sent to ten firms.

The Covers provide no clue as to why all-oil stowage was not adopted and the only criticisms noted are those expressed by the DNC. There may of course have been some natural conservatism which required

more careful consideration of all constructional details involved. Care was certainly exercised in the design of the fuel compartments for the completely oil-fired ships of the *Queen Elizabeth* class which were included in the next naval construction programme. A decision was made to increase the oil fuel stowage to 2450 tons and reduce the coal capacity to the same level. The DNC continued to investigate

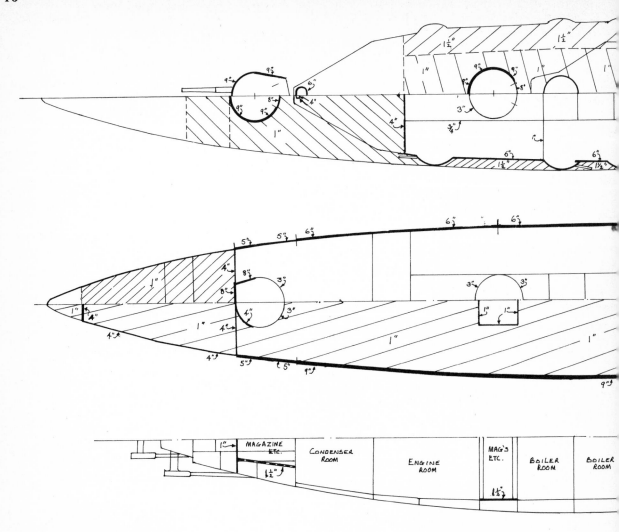

Deck plans showing armour thicknesses.
Shading shows areas of protective plating.

Sections showing armour thicknesses.

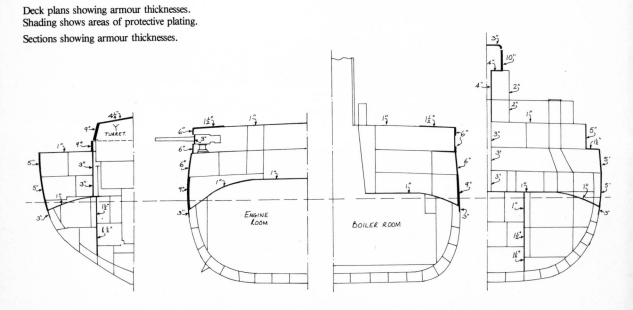

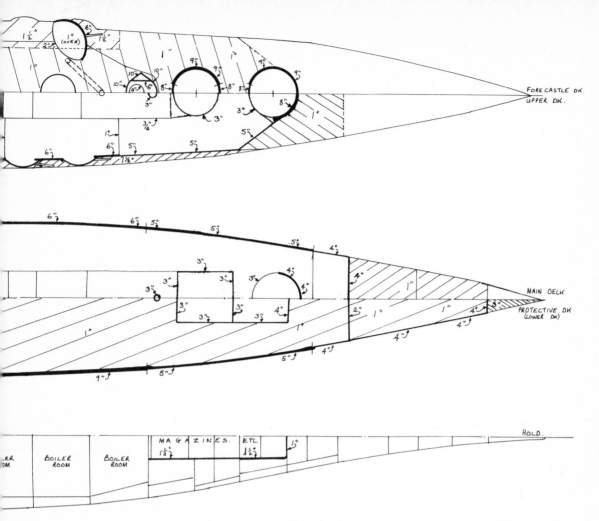

the possibilities of this development and on 20 December proposed to the Controller that the fuel stowage be further increased, principally by utilising the double bottom and other compartments next to the skin plating by fitting them with pipes and valves for use in an emergency.

This was approved on 21 December, the total fuel stowage being increased to an incredible 3480 tons oil and 3340 tons coal. Detailed calculations resulted in a further increase in maximum oil fuel stowage to 3800 tons, giving a total fuel stowage of 7140 tons compared with 4800 tons in the *Queen Mary*. Some of this increase was necessary to provide for the increased fuel consumption of the *Tiger's* more powerful machinery while the remainder served to increase the ship's endurance. But

the ship's full capacity was never employed and the maximum fuel normally carried during the First World War was 3240 tons of coal and 800 tons of oil. Unfortunately I have found no official figures for the *Tiger's* endurance but Parkes [4] gives a fuel consumption of 1245 tons per day at 59 500 HP. This is approximately equal to a speed of 24 knots which would give about 3300 nautical miles with 7140 tons of fuel. The equivalent figure for *Queen Mary* was about 2400 nautical miles.

Two more important modifications were made to the design before the ship was ordered. On 21 December it was decided to increase the height of the funnels to 81 ft above the load water line which added 5 ft to the funnels. This was intended to prevent any

repetition of the smoke interference problems experienced in recently completed capital ships. It was also decided in December or January to fit the ship with anti-rolling tanks. These were athwartship compartments containing free surface water. When the ship was rolling the movement of this water would in theory have had the affect of dampening the movement of the ship. It was intended that these should be fitted in all new capital ships, but in July 1912 it was decided to await the trials of the anti-rolling tanks in the battleship *Conqueror* before proceeding to fit them in other ships. In the case of the *Tiger* the tanks were not fitted. I do not know of results of the *Conqueror* trials, if they were carried out.

[4] *British Battleships 1860-1950* Dr Oscar Parkes

DISPLACEMENT 28,500 tons (load draught)

DIMENSIONS 704ft (oa), 660ft (pp) x 90ft 6in
x 28ft 6in (load, mean) 32ft
(deep, mean)

MACHINERY Brown-Curtis turbines, 4 shafts, 39
Babcock and Wilcox boilers, 85,000 SHP
=28 knots, 108,000 SHP = 29 knots

FUEL CAPACITY 3340 tons coal, 3800 tons oil fuel

ARMAMENT 8-13.5inch/45 cal Mk V in twin
Mk II mountings (80 rpg)
12—6 inch/45 cal, Mk VII on P VIII
mountings (200 rpg)
6—3pdr saluting guns (166 rpg)
5—0.303 inch Maxim machine guns (5000 rpg)
4—21inch submerged torpedo tubes,
20—21inch Mk II Whitehead torpedoes
6—14inch Mk X torpedoes for steam
boats.

1—12pdr, 8 cwt QF field gun and
carriage (200 rpg)

ARMOUR PROTECTIVE PLATING *Belt:* 9inch and 6inch amidships, 5inch
and 4inch forward, 5inch and 4inch aft,
3inch lower belt.

Bulkheads: 4inch and 2inch forward,
4inch aft.

Barbettes: 9inch and 8inch above belt 4inch, 3inch
and 1inch below belt.

Gunhouses: 9inch sides, $4\frac{1}{4}$ and $3\frac{1}{2}$inch
roof.

Conning Tower: 10inch sides, 3inch
roof, 4 inch floor, 2inch base

Conning tower hood and support: 3inch

Communication tube: 4inch and 3inch

Torpedo conning tower (aft): 6inch sides
3inch roof

Torpedo conning tower tube: 4inch

6inch gun battery: 6inch sides, 4inch
aft, 5inch forward.

6inch gun casemates: 6inch side, 2inch
back, 1inch roof.

6inch gun shields: 3inch

Forecastle deck: 1inch and $1\frac{1}{2}$inch
over 6inch gun battery

Upper deck: 1inch over citadel except
under 6inch gun battery.

Main deck: 1inch at ends

Lower deck: 1inch, 3inch at bow.

Protective bulkheads: 1inch and $1\frac{1}{2}$inch
abreast magazines and shell rooms.

TABLE 3 PARTICULARS OF TIGER AS FINALLY DESIGNED 1912

COMPLEMENT 1110

WEIGHTS:

LEGEND CONDITION:

General equipment	845 tons
Armament	3,660 tons
Machinery	5,630 tons
Engineers stores	125 tons
Coal	450 tons
Oil fuel	450 tons
Armour	7,400 tons
Hull	9,580 tons
Margin	100 tons
Water in anti-rolling tanks	250 tons
Total	**28,490 tons**

ORDINARY DEEP CONDITION

Legend displacement		28,490 tons
General equipment	+	125 tons
Coal	+	2,000 tons
Oil fuel	+	2,000 tons
Reserve feed water	+	620 tons
Water in overflow tank	+	80 tons
Water in anti-rolling tanks	+	145 tons
Total		**33,470 tons**

EXTREME DEEP CONDITION

Ordinary deep displacement		33,470 tons
Coal	+	890 tons
Oil fuel	+	1,350 tons
Total		**35,710 tons**

LIGHT CONDITION

Legend displacement		28,490 tons
General equipment	—	237 tons
Engineers stores	—	63 tons
Oil fuel	—	450 tons
Coal	—	450 tons
Water in anti-rolling tanks	—	250 tons
Total		**27,040 tons**

TABLE 4 STABILITY FIGURES FOR TIGER AS DESIGNED

	LIGHT	LEGEND	ORDINARY DEEP	EXTREME DEEP
GM	5ft	4.9ft	6.2ft	6.3ft
Angle of maximum stability	43°	43°	43°	44°
Range	**71°**		80°	86°

Note: 0.7 ft was taken off the GM in the deep conditions and 0.4ft in legend condition to allow for free surface water in the anti-rolling tanks. The GM as completed was 5ft 2inches in legend condition and 6ft 7inches in deep condition with ranges of 74°and 86° respectively.

1 The *Tiger* late in 1917, Note the aircraft hanger and platform on 'Q' turret, training scales on 'B' and 'Y' turrets and the dark panel painted on the side amidships.

2 The *Tiger* in 1919. Note flagstaff replaced on stern; Carley rafts on 'Q' turret, abreast searchlight towers and bridge structure.

TABLE 5

SPEED	28.38 knots	29.07 knots
SHP	91,103	104,635
RPM	267	278
DISPLACEMENT	28,990 tons	28,790 tons
NUMBER OF RUNS	6	4

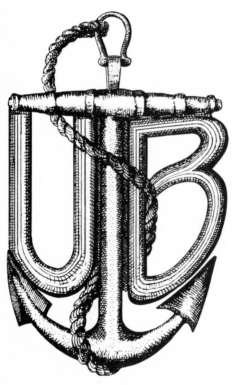

The symbol of the Austro-Hungarian submarine service.
Courtesy of the author

U 4 in Pola harbour, 1917. The operation of the 3.7cm QF gun on the forward edge of the tower was ridiculous: this gun had no recoil but the gunner had to balance on the handrails on the flanks of the tower. The cable clearly visible is a mine deflecting cable, below and less visible is the radio antenna. Note a *Tegetthoff* class battleship in the background.

Dr Aichelburg Collection

AUSTRO-HUNGARIAN SUBMARINES

by Erwin F Sieche

U 1 leaving Pola harbour 1914.
Dr Aichelburg Collection

Although man had tried to invent a submersible ship centuries earlier the accelerating development of technology and the unlimited belief in industrial progress which took place in the second half of the nineteenth century caused a renaissance of the idea. It is interesting that the rich ideas of these inventors were not matched by existing techniques; on the contrary, their inventions caused the development of the technology needed for their realisation.

At the beginning of 1904 the director of Austrian warship construction, Oberingenieur Paul Popper, suggested to the naval-technical committee (MTK = *Marinetechnisches Kommittee,* Pola) the design of a submarine. The development of an Austrian submarine by the MTK turned out to be very complicated due to a great many unsolved technical problems. At the beginning of 1905 the MTK presented a rough design for a single-hull boat with the dimensions 22.1 m x 3.60 m x 4.27 m. The Admiralty doubted the effectiveness of the design and decided to buy three different foreign designs. For every design two boats were to be ordered to be tested against each other, so the A-H navy would evaluate the

specifications for a submarine suitable to their special needs.

THE LAKE BOATS

In 1893 the American Simon Lake lost the competition of the US Navy Ordnance Bureau for a submarine-building contract. His concept of a submarine derived from a boat for peaceful exploring missions. His war-submarine relied on a hand-to-hand fighting system, could roll on wheels on the seabed, and from it divers could exit through a diving chamber to destroy ships and telegraph-cables by explosive charges. Later he incorporated the torpedo in his design, but the basic ideas were still unchanged.

In 1904 Lake's firm was visited by an A-H delegation and in 1906 he came to Pola to finish the contract on the building of *U.1* and *U.2* It was signed on 24 November 1906.

The boats were built to his plans at the naval dockyard, Pola (*Seearsenal* Pola). They had two retractable wheels and a diving chamber under the bow. The diving tanks were located on top of the cylindrical hull. This meant that a heavy ballast keel was necessary to provide vertical stability. As the diving tanks were situated above the waterline, they had to be flooded by pumps. At the first trials this took 14 minutes 37 seconds; later it was speeded up to 8 minutes. When running trials with both boats many technical problems arose. Poisoning

by exhaust fumes and gasoline vapour was a daily problem. As the gasoline engines could not be considered effective under war conditions and did not reach their contract power, the A-H Navy commissioned and paid only for the hulls and the armament. Thereafter new diesel engines were ordered at the Austrian *Maschinenfabrik* Leobersdorf, and until their delivery the original engines were leased for US $4544 per year. The Lake boats had variable-pitch propellers, four pairs of diving rudders which provided a high degree of underwater manoeuvrability. Once a boat was exactly trimmed and balanced it held its depth within a 20 cm oscillation without help from the rudders.

Diving trials showed that the hulls began to crush at 40 m so the trial commission recommended that a diving depth of 40 m should definately not be exceeded. The drop-shaped hull caused a strong bow-wave, and the boats tended to dip their bows under, so the deck and bow casing was rebuilt with a better hydrodynamic shape.

All this leads to the final conclusion that these boats were not sophisticated weapons, but they were exactly what the A-H Navy had ordered: experimental boats to show in extensive trials the reliability of a mass of new technical innovations. Some of these proved to be useless, eg, rolling on wheels on the seabed

Boat No		MTK project	U.1, 2	U. 3,4	5,6,12
TYPE		Austrian design	Lake	Germania	Holland
SYSTEM		single-hull	double-hull,	double-hull internal saddle tanks	single-hull
DSPL. IN METRIC TONS		134.5	229.7 248.9 after reconstr. 223.0 277.5	240 300	240 273
LENGTH	wl	22.6 m	30.48 m	43.2 m	32.1 m (oa.)
HULL	Ø	3.6 m	3.62 m	3.0 m	4.2 m
DRAUGHT		4.37 m	3.85 m	2.75 m	3.9 m
ENGINES		engines	2 gasoline engines tog. 720 HP 2 E-engines tog. 200 HP	2 4-cyl/2-stroke tog. 600 HP 2 E-engines tog. 200 HP	2 6-cyl/gasoline tog. 500 HP 2 E-engines tog. 230 HP
SPEED		9.5 7 kn	10.3 kn 6 kn	12 kn 8.5 kn⁻	10.75 kn 8.5 kn
ENDURANCE		950 m/6 kn	950 sm/6 kn 15 sm/5 kn.40 sm/2 kn	1200 sm/12 kn 40 sm/3 kn	800 sm/8.5 kn 48 sm/6 kn
T-ARMAMENT			2 TT 45 cm/bow 1 TT 45 cm/stern	2 TT 45 cm/bow	2 TT 45 cm/bow
SUPPLY			5 torpedoes	3 torpedoes	4 torpedoes
CREW			18	21	19

U 2's conning tower. The tripod on the right of the tower carried the steering wheel during surface manoeuvres, such as when entering harbour. The funnel-like structure on the left is a ventilation mast. Note the primitive type second periscope.

Pawlik Collection

turned out to be nearly impossible, and today every modern snorkel diver knows more about underwater visibility than the inventor of 1890 who planned underwater-observation bull's eyes.

Operational History of the Lake Boats

U.1:

2.7.1907 keel laid; 10.2.1909 launched; 1910 trials; 5.4.1910 both electric motors damaged through flooding; 15.4.1911 commissioned; 1911-1914 training boat, ie, ten training cruises per month; 13.1.1914 rammed in Fasana Channel by A-H cruiser *St. Georg,* periscope destroyed; end of 1914- early 1915 installation of diesel-engines and new batteries; up to 4.10.1915 training boat; 2.11.1915

based at Trieste, reconnaissance patrols; 22.12.1917 based at Pola naval base; 11.1.1918 declared obsolete; training boat based at Brioni Island submarine base; ceded as war reparation to Italy 1920; scrapped at Pola.

U.2:

18.7.1907 keel laid; 3.4.1909 launched; 1909-10 trials; 22.6.1911 commissioned; up to 1915 training boat, ie, ten training cruises per month; 24.1.-4.6.1915 refit at Pola, new conning tower; 7.8.1915 based at Trieste, reconnaissance patrols; 11.1.1918 declared obsolete; training boat based at Brioni Island submarine base; ceded as war reparation to Italy 1920; scrapped at Pola.

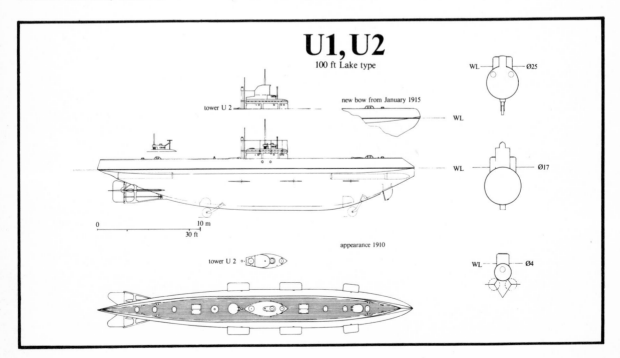

U1, U2
100 ft Lake type

tower U 2

new bow from January 1915

WL

WL Ø25

WL Ø17

0   10 m
30 ft

appearance 1910

tower U 2

WL Ø4

U 4 undated picture, probably taken in Pola Harbour.
Imperial War Museum

THE GERMANIA BOATS

In the growing Imperial German high seas fleet created by Tirpitz there was no place for the concept of submarine warfare. Not until the 1905 official *Torpedoinspektion*, under the direction of Dipl Ing Gustav Berling, did the German Navy begin to develop operational submarines. As other navies already had submarines in service, the *Germaniawerft* at Kiel tried to avoid falling behind by designing submarines for foreign navies.

In March 1904 two A-H naval officers watched the trials of the submarine *Forelle* at Kiel/Eckernförde. At a second contract meeting at the *Germaniawerft* the A-H delegation received the impression that everything was being done to get a building contract but technical questions were deliberately obscured.

The A-H Admiralty therefore refused to purchase Germania-built submarines. So shocked was the *Germaniawerft* that it offered some designs without cost in June 1906. A short time later positive reports on the Germania-built boats for

Czarist Russia reached Austria, and it was decided to buy two boats. Both boats were built at Kiel and towed to Pola via Gibraltar. They were of double-hull type with internal saddle-tanks.

Although the German designers had evaluated the best hull-shape in extensive model trials, these boats had constant trouble with their diving rudders. The rudder fins were changed in size and shape, and finally the bow rudders were removed and a fixed stern flap was installed, but the outbreak of war stopped further experiments. Because of their greater displacement these boats had better seagoing qualities and living conditions than their competitors. Considering that this was one of the first designs of *Germaniawerft* without extensive practical experience, these boats showed a high degree of effectiveness, and *U.4* had the longest operational history of all A-H submarines. This leads to the conclusion that the Germania type was a very modern and well-balanced design.

Operational History of the Germania Boats

U.3:
12.3.1907 keel laid; 20.8.1908 launched; 24.1.1909 arrived at Pola in tow, trials; 12.9.1909 commissioned; 1910-14 training boat, ie ten training cruises per month; 22.8.1914 based at Brioni Island submarine base; 27.9.1914 based at Cattaro naval base, reconnaissance cruises; April 1915 3.7 cm QF gun installed; 10.8.1915 left Cattaro for action north of Brindisi; 12.8.1915 rammed during unsuccessful torpedo attack on Italian armed merchant cruiser *Città di Catania* (3500 BRT; 2 x 12 cm; 6 x 7.5 cm), periscope destroyed, when surfacing shelled by escorting French destroyer *Bisson* and depth-charged, damaged on seabed; 13.8.1915 when surfacing hit by French destroyer, *Bisson* (765 t; 4 x 6.5 cm, 4 TT) and sunk: 7 killed, 14 survivors captured.

U.4:
12.3.1907 keel laid; 20.11.1908 launched; 19.4.1909 arrived at Pola in tow, trials; 29.8.1908

commissioned; 1910-14 training boat, ie ten training cruises per month; 27.9.1914 based at Cattaro naval base, reconnaissance cruises; December 1914 radio equipment installed; 19.2.1915 three Montenegrin captured; April 1915 3.7 cm QF gun installed; 24.5.1915 unsuccessful torpedo attack on Italian *Puglia* type cruiser in the Gulf of Drin; 9.6.1915 British cruiser *Dublin* (5400 t; 8 x 15.2 cm, 4 x 4.7 cm, 2 TT) damaged by torpedo; 18.7.1915 Italian armoured cruiser *Giuseppe Garibaldi* (7350 t; 1 x 25 cm, 2 x 20 cm, 14 x 15 cm, 4 TT) torpedoed off Ragusavecchia (now Cavtat): 53 killed, 525 survivors; 14.5.1915 searched for lost sister *U.3;* 8.11.1915 unsuccessful attack on British *Diamond* type cruiser; 9.12.1915 one Albanian schooner captured in the Gulf of Drin; December 1915 new periscopes and gyro compass installed; 3.1.1916 one Albanian schooner captured; 2.2.1916 French steamer *Jean Bart* (475 BRT) torpedoed and sunk off Cape Laghi; 7.2.1916 unsuccessful attack on British cruiser of *Birmingham* type; 26-27.3.1916 searched for lost A-H submarine *U.24;* 30.3.1916

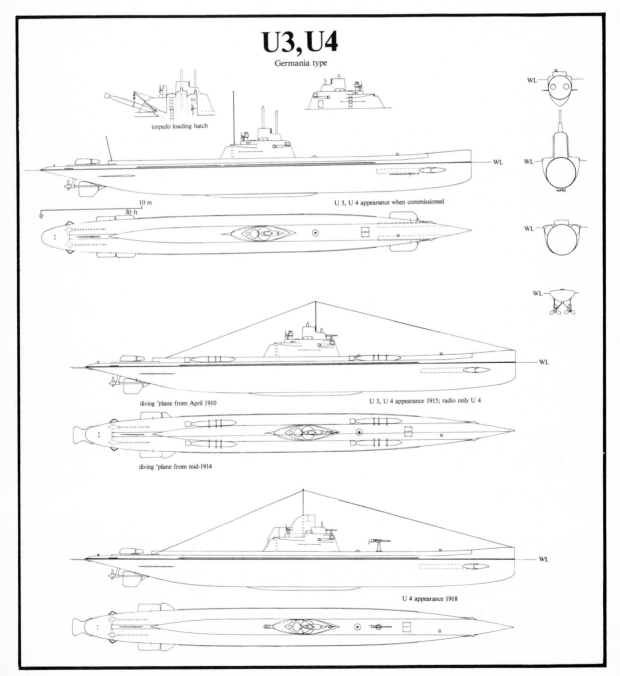

U3, U4

Germania type

torpedo loading hatch

10 m

30 ft

U 3, U 4 appearance when commissioned

diving 'plane from April 1910

U 3, U 4 appearance 1915; radio only U 4

diving 'plane from mid-1914

U 4 appearance 1918

WL

British schooner *John Pritchard of Carnar* (271 BRT) sunk with explosive charges off Antipaxos Island; July 1916 7 cm cal/26 gun installed; 2.8.1916 unsuccessful attack on Italian cruiser of *Nino Brixio* type; 5.8.1916 unsuccessfully attacked by enemy submarine with two torpedoes; 12.8.1916 Italian schooner *Ponte Maria* (188 BRT) torpedoed and sunk off Brindisi; 12.8.1916 unsuccessful attack on enemy submarine west of Cape Laghi; 14.8.1916 British steamer *Inverberbie* (4390 BRT) torpedoed and sunk off Cape Nau; 30.5.1917 Italian steamer *Italia* (1305 BRT) torpedoed and sunk off Corfu Island; 19.6.1917 French steamer *Edouarde Corbière* (475 BRT) and Greek steamer *Cefira* (411 BRT) torpedoed and sunk off Taranto; 12.7.1917 French salvage tug *Berthilde* (1500 BRT) torpedoed and sunk off Cape Stilo; September 1917 new bulwark on conning tower fitted; 1.11.1918 final return to Pola; ceded as war reparation to France, scrapped 1920.

THE HOLLAND BOATS

The Irish-American John Paul Holland had designed submarines from the 1890s and earlier. After he won a contract for building submarines for the US Navy in 1893 his company, the Holland Boat Company at Newport, Connecticut, became one of the leading builders of submarines and stayed in the business for decades.

The Fiume-based firm of Whitehead, which had become the developer of the Luppis torpedo, decided to enter the submarine business and bought a licence from Holland to build his submarines. The first two boats were partially assembled in the United States and riveted together at Whitehead's in Fiume which caused a lot of trouble. The third boat was built on speculation and comprised a better development of all mechanical and electrical systems. This unit was named *SS.3* and was offered to the A-H Navy too, but she was refused because of the trials programme. Whitehead offered *SS.3* to the navies of Peru, Portugal, Netherlands, Brazil, Bulgaria and to the A-H Navy a second time. When war broke out Austria bought the unsold boat and provisionally commissioned it as *U.7*. After the end of August 1914 it was definitely commissioned as *U.12*. The Holland type featured a distinctive tear-drop hull bearing a strong resemblance to modern nuclear subs. It had an interesing construction of the torpedo-tube hatches: these were clover-leaf shaped and rotated on a central axis.

Operational History of the Holland boats

U.5:
9.4.1908 keel laid; 10.2.1909 launched; 17.8.1909 towed to Pola for final outfit; 1.4.1910 commissioned, training boat, ie, ten training cruises per month; 1.5.1911 shown to a delegation of Peruvian naval officers; 10.6.1912 trials with a kite balloon to evaluate underwater sighting of hull painting; 22.8.1914 based at Brioni

U 6 in Cattaro Bay, 1915. Note the massive towing hook at the bow.
Dr Aichelburg Collection

Island submarine base; 22.1.1914 based at Cattaro naval base; 3.11.1914 unsuccessful attack on French battleship squadron off Punta Stilo; 6.12.1914 radio receiver and 3.7 cm cal/23 QF gun installed; 27.5.1915 French armoured cruiser *Leon Gambetta* (12 250 t; 4 x 19 cm, 16 x 16 cm, 24 x 4.7 cm; 2 TT) torpedoed and sunk off Santa Maria di Leuca: 648 killed, 173 survivors; 1.6.1915 searched for lost A-H seaplane L 41; 2.7.1915 new 4.7 cm QF gun installed instead of 3.7 cm, complete radio station installed; 5.8.1915 Italian submarine *Nereide* (225/303 t; 3 TT) torpedoed and sunk off Pelagosa Island: 17 killed, no survivors; 29.8.1915 Greek steamer *Cefalonia* (1034 BRT) captured off Durazzo; 26.4.1916 unsuccessful gun attack on merchant convoy in the Otranto Strait; 7.6.1916 unsuccessful attack on Italian *Indomito* type destroyer; 8.6.1916 Italian armed merchant cruiser *Principe Umberto* (7919

BRT) torpedoed and sunk off Linguetta: about 1750 killed, ? survivors; September-November 1917 refit: new conning tower, new gun 7.5 cm cal/30; 16.5.1917 during training cruise in the Fasana Channel struck mine with the stern, sunk: 6 killed, 13 survivors; 20-24.6.1916 raised from 36 m; 22.8.1918 recommissioned after refit; 25.3.1919 transferred to Venice, inspected by British military commissions; ceded as war reparation to Italy 1920; scrapped.

U.6:
21.2.1908 keel laid; 12.6.1909 launched; 1.7.1909 commissioned, training boat, ie ten training cruises per month; 7.11.1910 demonstrated to a Norwegian naval delegation; 26.6.1912 when surfacing after deep diving trial rammed by submarine tender *Pelikan;* 29.12.1914 based at Cattaro naval base; December 1915 installation of 3.7 cm cal/23 QF gun; 23.2.1916 unsuccessful attack on Italian type *Indomito* destroyer;

18.3.1916 French destroyer *Renaudin* (720 t; 2 x 10 cm, 4 x 6.5 cm; 2 TT) torpedoed and sunk off Cape Laghi: ? killed, ? survivors; soon after, unsuccessful attack on French *Bisson* type destroyer; 13.5.1916 trapped in submarine net during break through the Otranto barrage and scuttled by crew: entire crew taken prisoner.

U.12:
1909 keel laid; 14.3.1911 launched; bought by the A-H Navy after war began; 21.8.1914 commissioned; 14.11.1914 3.7 cm cal/23 QF gun installed; 7.12.1914 based at Cattaro naval base; 21.12.1914 French battleship *Jean Bart* (23 470 t; 2 x 30.5 cm, 22 x 13.8 cm, 4 x 4.7 cm, 4 TT) damaged by two torpedoes in the Otranto Strait; 22.3.1915 two Montenegrin schooners captured; 31.3.1916 one Montenegrin schooner captured; 28.6.1916 during refit two additional torpedo tubes installed outboard on the forward casing; about 12.8.1916 sunk by

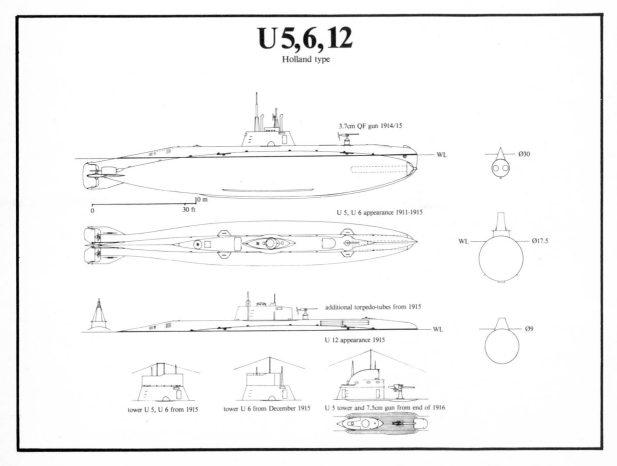

U 5, 6, 12

Holland type

3.7cm QF gun 1914/15

WL

Ø30

0 m

0   30 ft

U 5, U 6 appearance 1911-1915

WL

Ø17.5

additional torpedo-tubes from 1915

WL

Ø9

U 12 appearance 1915

tower U 5, U 6 from 1915

tower U 6 from December 1915

U 5 tower and 7.5cm gun from end of 1916

mine when trying to break into the harbour of Venice: entire crew (17) lost; raised by Italy at the end of 1916 and scrapped in the Venice naval arsenal; victims buried at the cemetery of San Michele in Venice.

1 *U 1:* conning tower with embossed pennant number. Note that the towers of the first boats were extremely low.
Dr Aichelburg Collection

2 *U 12* entering Pola harbour, 1914. Note the shape of the tower of this boat which was developed by Whitehead as a private venture and differs slightly from her sister-boats. The base ring for a 3.7cm QF pivot is fixed on deck.
Dr Aichelburg Collection

3 *U 5* in Cattaro Bay, 1915. The bridge is sheltered by a canvas bulwark. The conventional air intakes were later removed.
Dr Aichelburg Collection

1

2

3

SMS U-14 ex Curie

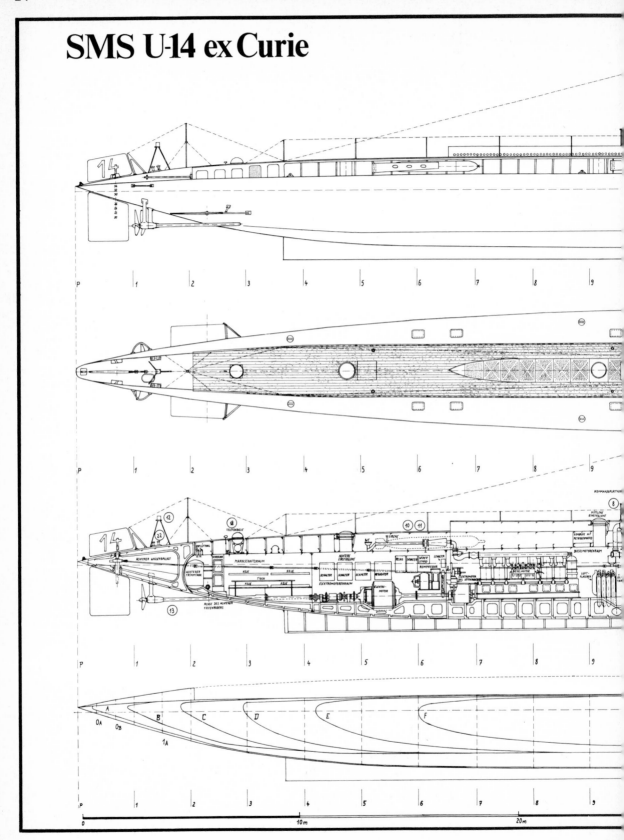

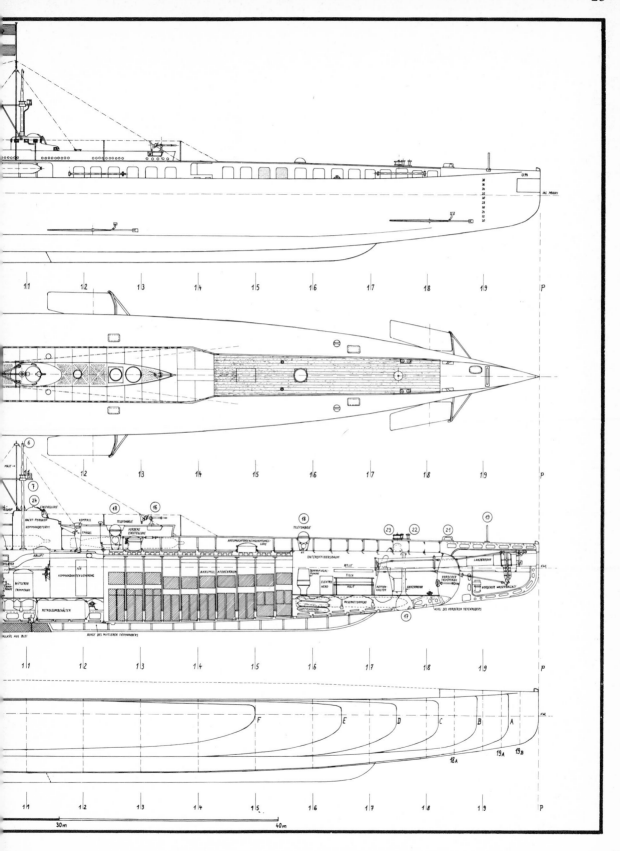

30m

40m

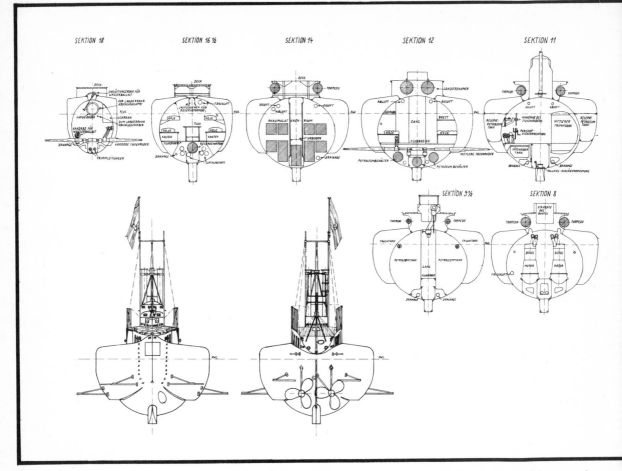

GUN ARMAMENT

As attacks on merchant ships increased, quick-firing guns were installed. From the beginning these were 3.7 cm, later 4.7 cm. *U.5* was upgunned with a German 7 cm/30 cal submarine gun during a major refit.

VARIATIONS IN CONNING TOWERS

For all three types the first intention of the constructors was a real submarine, so they built small, low observation platforms. Later the range of vision turned out to be too short and in addition these towers were very uncomfortable, wet and dangerous for the bridge watches, so all A-H submarines were fitted with bulwarks of different shapes. During major refits some boats received new, higher towers with an enlarged space and protecting bulwarks.

RADIO EQUIPMENT

When the first boats were built radio telegraphy was in its first stage of development too. As the sets became more compact the boats were subsequently equipped with radios.

Note: the antenna-like wires that can be seen on the drawings are 'jumping wires' or mine-deflecting cables; the real antennae were on retractable masts and so thin that one can hardly see them in pictures.

CONCLUSION

Looking at the technology of the first submarines of the A-H Navy, we find trend-setting innovations like variable-pitch propellers, teardrop hull, diver-locks and retractable ventilation masts (which would have become a real snorkel if it had been developed further). But the difficulties of perfecting these items were not solved. Also the machinery and the periscopes needed further development, but one must keep in mind that these units were only prototypes. German submarine ratings who visited and examined the early Austrian boats were surprised by their primitive nature and said that they would refuse to make a sortie in such a vessel.

Despite these deficiencies these subs performed admirably and achieved much in the Adriatic war: enemy battleships were forced to leave the Adriatic Sea, and no major action was ever carried against the Yugoslavian coast. The Italian battlefleet left the Adriatic as well and for the whole war remained useless, in safe but remote bases.

Because of the war situation and the alliance, Austria was forced to use German subs and submarine designs with two exceptions: the raised French

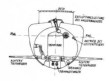

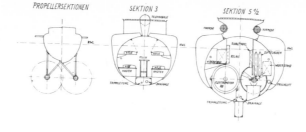

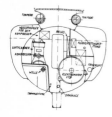

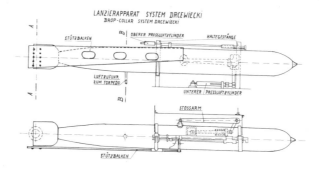

ABOVE AND PREVIOUS PAGES:
Details from Friedrich Prasky's superbly detailed modelmakers' plans of the Austrian *U 14* ex-French *Curie*. Copies of the plan can be obtained from Mr Prasky at Feuchterslebengasse 69-71/5, A-1100 Wien, Austria.

Curie (later the Austrian *U.14*), and the Whitehead built *Havmanden* type.

COLOUR SCHEME

Up to spring 1914 all Austrian subs were painted light blue-grey, but submarines could easily be detected by aeroplanes. On 29 April 1914 trials were carried out with *U.4* and the seaplane *E.17*. Dark blue turned out to be the best underwater colour, but on the other hand the silhouette above water was too dark. Because of a British fleet visit to Pola harbour (from this occasion dates a frequently published picture with the A-H battleship *Erzherzog Franz Ferdinand* and a 32 ft cutter with the British White Ensign in the foreground) the original painting was restored. After war broke out all boats were painted dark blue with a large white pennant number on the tower.

In spring 1915 the sides of the towers were painted light grey to make the boats less visible above water. Pictures taken in 1915 show some boats with a multicolour dazzle painting, but the colour composition is unknown. From 1916 the boats had no number painted on their tower. In August 1918 *U.4* and *U.5* had a light grey hull and tower.

SOURCES AND ACKNOWLEDGEMENTS

I would like to thank specifically Dr. Wladimir Aichelburg for allowing me to use material from his unpublished manuscript *Die KuK Unterseebootwaffe 1904-1918*; without his assistance and permission this article would not be so complete. When he researched the technical and operational history of the first A-H subs, it turned out that the few earlier publications on this subject were often erroneous because they did not rely on the official sources of the Austrian Kriegsarchiv in Vienna.

A brief article on *U.1* and *U.2* with my drawing was published in the Austrian naval magazine *Marine — Gestern, heute* (June 1976).

Champions of the

No single class of warship has had more influence on American policies and naval tactics than the 24 *Essex* class fleet carriers. They possessed those factors necessary to insure American dominance of all of the world's oceans: overwhelming numbers, durability, adaptability and good aircraft complement.

Thirty-five years after the commissioning of the first ship, *Essex,* the magnificent *Lexington (CV16)* still sails the oceans. While the majority of the class have been scrapped, a handful are still in reserve and one ship, *Yorktown,* has been made part of a naval and maritime museum in South Carolina. Fortunately, there are a number of groups actively negotiating for the preservation of additional *Essexes*. The most prominent of these groups is Odysseys In Flight Inc., a non-profit organization preparing an aerospace and naval museum complex in the North Eastern United States.

It would take volumes to document adequately the *Essexes'* technical and operational careers. It is the primary purpose of this article to identify the wartime appearances of the *Essex* sisterships which took an active part in the Pacific War. It will also briefly cover all of the units which were completed too late to see any action and a few of the many postwar modifications. For a better understanding of the WW2 *Essexes,* it is necessary to cover the entire class.

This will include prominent gun positions, radars, other visible structural variations and camouflage paint schemes. Practically each *Essex* can be identified by some dominant feature, or arrangement which was unique to that specific ship, at a specific time.

IDENTIFIABLE CHARACTERISTICS

To eliminate repetition, the following list is intended to explain those characteristics which will constantly be referred to:

1 **Short Bow** Ten ships were completed with a near vertical stem. These units carried only a single quadruple 40mm AA mount directly over the stem. The flight deck actually overhung the mount, restricting its field of fire.

2 **The Early Bridge** The first eight units were completed with four quad 40mm mounts on the island, two forward and two aft of the funnel. The foremost mount was sited immediately forward of a rather small and cramped flag bridge.

3 **Off-Centerline Single Quad 40mm On The Fantail** Also carried by the first eight units, this feature was common only to those ships which carried the early bridge.

4 **Hangar Deck Catapult** Never installed on the first two units, it was carried by the third to the eighth completed units, in conjunction with the above three features. The catapult was fixed awthartships on the forward hangar deck, just aft of the fo'csle deck break. The catapult's most noticeable features were the hinged extension arms, on both the port and starboard sides. The port side extension was hinged on an extended outboard platform. The starboard extension arm was flush to the ship's side. Both extension arms were hinged in the 'up' position when not in use. Units carrying a hangar catapult were completed with only one flight deck catapult. When it was removed (from all six units), a

Hornet (CV-12) in dazzle camouflage design 3A, at Pearl Harbor.

Pacific The Essex class carriers

by Lawrence Sowinski

second flight deck catapult was added. Catapults were also known as 'cats'.

5 Starboard Quarter, Hangar Deck Level, Quad 40mm AA Mounts These two mounts were added to the same six ships which carried the hangar deck catapult. Since all the *Essexes* were built on the East Coast of the United States, no unmoveable outboard extensions could be fitted which would not allow passage through the Panama Canal locks. For this purpose the port side (flight deck-edge) elevator was designed to hinge upright.

6 SK Radar Antenna This was the largest antenna carried on the wartime *Essexes*. It was fitted on the first ten units to be completed. Often referred to as a big 'bedspring', it was rectangular in shape. It was sited in three different positions and these tended to depend on the building yard. The first three ships completed at Newport News, Virginia *(CV9, 10 & 11)* carried the SK on top of the tripod mast, in front of the topmast, on the radar platform. The first three units completed at Quincy, Massachussetts *(CV16, 17 & 18)* fitted the SK outboard on the funnel's starboard side, on an extended platform. The last four SK-equipped ships all carried the 'bedspring' on top of the radar platform, but abaft the topmast. The smaller SM dish antenna generally dominated the forward position on the radar platform.

7 SC and SC-2 Radar Antenna This was a comparatively small 'bedspring' antenna. While the SK was higher than it was wider, the SC was wider than higher. Initially, it was close to its base, but was later raised skyward, often on a lattice mast. The majority of the other antennae were too small to deal with individually.

8 Starboard Radio Lattice Masts The first four units *(CV9, 16, 10 & 17)* were completed with five radio masts along the flight deck's starboard side. Three were forward of the island, two aft. All the remaining wartime units carried four (only two forward). Refitted units often had the two after masts removed. All the masts hinged down during flight operations.

9 Outboard Quad 40mm Mounts With the need for increased anti-aircraft fire power, a number of additional medium range AA mounts were installed. Seven mounts were added on outboard extensions; three below the island structure on the starboard side and two on the starboard stern quarter, on the hangar deck, in the same position as the inboard mounts discussed in **5**. The difference was that the outboard mounts were on extended sponsons, with clear fields of fire. The six units with the inboard mounts eventually had them moved outboard. Two outboard quads were added to the flight deck's port quarter. Prior to passage through the Panama Canal, all

seven outboard quad mounts had to be removed.

10 Long Bow Units The remaining 14 sisterships were all long bow units. While the waterline length remained the same, the stem was raked forward in a clipper fashion. As the flare was greatly increased the bow platform could be widened; this improved seakeeping and allowed room for two quad 40mm to be fitted. The flight deck was not lengthened and so both mounts enjoyed a considerably improved field of fire.

11 Later Units The last 15 ships were commissioned with two flight deck catapults and no hangar cat. The port side hangar deck platform remained, but it was used to carry two quad 40mm instead.

These units also carried a number of other modifications: two quad 40mm on an extended fantail platform; an extended flag bridge (the foremost quad 40mm was dropped to make room) and, except for *CV14* and *19*, a large SK-2 dish antenna was fitted in place of the SK. All eight of the early units eventually received most of these modifications.

12 Paint Schemes Three major types of camouflage paint schemes were applied to the wartime ships. The US Navy referred to camouflage schemes as 'measures', and specific types were identified by a code number (12, 21, 32, 33, etc).

Carrier decks and horizontal surfaces were not repainted

1 Close up of *Lexington*'s (CV-16) radar after her first Puget Sound refit. The SK is the large bedspring between the tripod foremast and the new mainmast. The SC-2 is the smaller bedspring (directly behind the SK) on the raised lattice mast. The SM is on the front of the radar platform, on top of the tripod.

2 *Yorktown* (CV-10) was the first unit to carry a hangar catapult. In this view, the catapult extension arm is in the 'down' position. The tubs for the two starboard quarter 40mm quads are just visible under the flight deck.

1

2

32

1 *Ticonderoga* (CV-14) burns and lists after two kamikaze hits on 21 January 1945. Compare her starboard pattern to that carried by *Yorktown.*

2 *Yorktown* (CV-10) after her refit at Puget Sound. All five starboard outboard quad 40s are clearly visible, as is the enlarged fantail sponson. CV-10 remained in dazzle Design 10A till the late spring of '45 at which time she was painted into Ms21.

3 *Intrepid* (CV-11) after her February '45 refit. She was the first *Essex* in Ms12. Unfortunately, the negative is in very poor condition.

1

2

3

when the measures were changed. Flight decks were stained, not painted.

Measure 21 was the only single-color camouflage used by the *Essexes* during WW2. It was an overall solid medium-to-dark blue/gray (known as navy blue). In photographs, it appears as a medium gray (in bright sun) or a dark gray (in overcast skies). The first six *Essexes* were completed in measure 21.

Dazzle Pattern Measures The *Essexes* carried two dazzle measures, but it is difficult for a casual observer to identify one from the other. It was the range of colors which determined which measure was actually carried. The same pattern design could appear on several different ships, with the same color range (measure) or a different color range.

Dazzle measure 33 was carried by five *Essexes (CV10, 12, 14, 18 and 38)*. *Hornet (CV12)* carried Design 3A (A for aircraft carrier). The other four ships all were painted in Design 10A. The darkest color

was never darker than navy blue, the lightest was either pale or light gray.

Dazzle measure 32 colors were painted on nine *Essexes (CV9, 11, 13, 15, 17, 19, 20, 31 and 36)*. Five separate designs were carried by these nine ships. The lightest color was either light or haze gray. The darkest color was usually dull black, although *CV31* and *36* carried only navy blue).

The dazzle measures were designed to confuse enemy submarines and low-flying torpedo bombers. However, the sudden introduction of *kamikaze* warfare left the carriers somewhat conspicuous to suiciders diving from high angles, and so measure 21 quickly came back into use for want of a better camouflage. Measure 12 was a two-color scheme intended to be more effective than either measure 21 or the dazzle measures. It used a two-tone system of ocean gray (medium) over navy blue (dark).

Instead of discussing each individual ship from start to finish, I have categorized their appearance

changes in chronological order. For those readers unfamiliar with the US Navy practice of hull numbers, keep in mind that these numbers remained the same and did not fluctuate the way most other navies changed pendant numbers.

THE EARLY UNITS

The first two *Essexes* were nearly identical. *Essex (CV9)* completed at Newport News Shipbuilding and Drydock Co, Virginia on 31 December 1942. *Lexington (CV16)* came out of Bethlehem Steel at Quincy, Massachussetts, on 17 March 1943. Both short bow units had early bridges, single fantail quad and five radio masts. The respective position of their large SK antennae enables identification of one from the other. *Essex* carried the bedspring forward on the radar platform, while 'Lex's' was fitted outboard on the funnel. *Essex* also carried a stump mainmast, whereas 'Lex' did not.

Both ships were easily identifiable from the next six units since neither carried hangar catapults or starboard quarter quads.

The next two units were identical to each other, except for the position of the SK antennas.

1

1 *Essex* (CV-9) at Newport News on 19 December 1942. The SK bedspring antenna has yet to be added to the platform on top of the tripod.

2 *Wasp* (CV-18) after her Puget Sound refit. The two port quarter outboard mounts are visible just below the flight deck level.

3 *Lexington* (CV-16) in the Pacific after her January 1944 refit. She was the first of her class to carry the seven outboard quad 40s.

4 *Intrepid* (CV-11) off Norfolk during November '43. Note the single, off centreline quad 40 on the fantail and the two quads along the hangar deck's starboard stern quarter.

2

3

4

1

1 *Hornet* (CV-12) at Ulithi in heavily weathered camouflage. This same starboard pattern (Design 3A) was also worn by *Intrepid* and *Hancock*. The hangar catapult extension arm is in the 'down' position.

2 *Franklin* (CV-13) leaves Norfolk on 4 May 1944 with her port side freshly repainted into Design 3A. Note the new extended flag bridge. The hangar catapult extension arm has been removed.

All photos US official, courtesy of the author

Yorktown (CV10) came out of Newport News (15 April 1943) with her SK in the same position as *Essex*. Out of Quincy came *Bunker Hill (CV17),* matching 'Lex's' SK position 24 May 1943). Both *CV10 & 17* were short bow units with early bridges, stump mainmasts, single fantail quad, five radio masts and measure 21. However, these two carriers introduced the hangar catapult and two quads on the starboard stern quarter.

The fifth unit, *Intrepid (CV11)* was commissioned on 16 August 1943 out of Newport News. She was identical to *Yorktown* except that she initiated the practice of carrying four radio masts; only two were installed forward of the island. When *Intrepid* departed for the Pacific in late November 1943 her SK had been moved from atop the radar platform, down to outboard of the funnel. It will be noted later that her SK would be moved a third and final time, during a 1944 repair and refit.

Quincy completed the sixth *Essex* on 24 November 1943. *Wasp (CV18)* was an exact match for *Intrepid* (with the refitted SK) except for the absence of a stump mainmast; however, she retained this appearance for only a short time.

Hornet (CV12) was commissioned

five days after *Wasp*. Newport News built this, the seventh short-bow *Essex*. While she carried the standard features: early bridge, single fantail quad 40mm, hangar catapult, starboard quarter quad 40mm and only four radio masts, *Hornet* also introduced two new modifications. First, her SK was positioned behind the topmast, on the rear side of the radar platform. This was to become the standard SK position for the next three units, the last units to fit the 'bedspring'. Second, and most important, was the introduction of dazzle camouflage patterns in the *Essex* class, replacing measure 21. *Hornet* painted up into dazzle Design 3A, with measure 33 colors of pale gray, haze gray and navy blue, making CV12 unique. While two and a half more *Essexes* were painted in this same design, only *Hornet* wore the lighter measure 33 colors. Also, only *Hornet* wore this design with all the standard early features, early bridge, hangar cat, etc.

In the Pacific, *Lexington* was damaged by a Japanese aerial torpedo during December 1943. Permanent repairs were made at Puget Sound (Bremerton, Wash) and while there she was fitted with additional AAs. This was to become standard for practically

2

every *Essex* unit undergoing a refit in Pearl Harbor or on the West Coast. Lex's medium range AA was more than doubled, the number of quad 40mm rising from 8 to 17 mounts. This was a tremendous increase in topside weight, but was considered essential. Seven of these were outboard quad 40mm, two on the port stern quarter and five along the starboard side. She was the only early bridge *Essex* to carry these seven outboard mounts.

Additionally, a platform with two quad 40mm was added in the same position as the port side catapult extension (on the third to eighth units). More radars were added to the island, along with a mainmast.

While units in the Atlantic and Pacific were beginning to paint up in dazzle camouflage, 'Lex' remained in measure 21, and was to become unique because of this; eventually, she would be the only large fleet carrier not in dazzle.

Back in the Atlantic, *Franklin (CV13)* was the eighth unit of the class to be completed, at Newport News on 31 January 1944. Structurally, she was an exact match for *Hornet* except that she carried a noticeably different camouflage, Design 6A. Measure 32 colors were used: light gray, ocean

gray and dull black. This was one of the earliest pattern designs prepared by the Navy's camouflage department, and its port side was very elaborate.

Meanwhile, the *Essex* class in the Pacific began to replace their measure 21 schemes with dazzle patterns. Some time between February and April, *Bunker Hill* painted up Design 6A, probably at Pearl Harbor. She and *Franklin* were the only two *Essexes* to carry this design. Even though both ships were oceans apart, they were now very similar. These dazzle-painted ships could be identified from one another by:
1 *Bunker Hill* carried a stump mainmast, *Franklin* did not
2 *Bunker Hill's* SK was fitted off the funnel, *Franklin's* was abaft the topmast, on the radar platform
3 *Bunker Hill* carried five radio masts, *Franklin* only four.

During March 1944 *Wasp (CV18)* was painted in dazzle Design 10A while still at Boston. *Yorktown* received the same design at about the same time while at Pearl Harbor, and eventually, four *Essexes* would wear this design. *Wasp* was soon in the Pacific alongside *Yorktown,* both could be identified individually as *Wasp* had only four radio masts, no mainmast and the SK outboard, off the funnel.

Another *Essex* carrier fell victim to a Japanese aerial torpedo, during March 1944 after an attack on Truk; *Intrepid* limped back to Pearl Harbor, and then headed for permanent repairs on the West Coast.

In April 1944, *Essex* completed a refit at San Francisco. Of her entire class, she was the only unit to carry dazzle Design 6/10D, the only two-color (light gray and dull black) design carried by any US carrier. Structurally, the flat bridge was extended forward (the island's foremost quad and its director were removed). The stump mainmast was also removed. The radar platform was enlarged and the SC-2 was fitted abaft the topmast. The SK was moved to the funnel. A port side platform was built in the position occupied by the catapult extension (on the six later units). Two quads were added to this platform. At the same time that 'Lex' was having all seven outboard quads added, *Essex* had only two mounts added on the starboard quarter. Incredible as it may sound, both mounts were installed in the obsolete inboard positions, with restricted fields of fire. Even more incredible, *Essex* remained this way for the remainder of the war. She was the only unit of the original eight early *Essex* class never to carry any outboard quads.

The battle of Tsu-Shima

БУЙНЫЙ
Bujnij

by
N J M Campbell

The Russian destroyer *Bujnij* at speed.
CPL W/5/001

Few naval battles, apart from Jutland, have been more often described than the battle of Tsushima, the culminating action of the Russo-Japanese war at sea. Yet no account appreciates the real puzzle of the battle: how the Japanese managed to annihilate the Russian fleet with only 446 12inch shells from their most powerful guns.

THE RUSSO-JAPANESE WAR

The war began on the night of 8/9 February 1904 with a surprise destroyer attack on the Russian ships anchored in the Port Arthur roads. This was a partial success only, but the two best Russian battleships the *Retvisan* and *Tsessarevitch* were put out of action until late May/early June, having to be repaired with the use of cofferdams as there was no dock at Port Arthur that would take them. The night attack was followed up by a rather desultory daylight gunnery action which achieved little. At the outset the main Russian fleet (Vice-Admiral Stark) based on Port Arthur comprised 7 battleships, 1 armoured and 6 light cruisers, of which 4 were large, and 25 destroyers, while 3 armoured and 1 large light cruiser with 10 sea-going and 7 other torpedo boats were at Vladivostock. Including ships that would shortly be available, the Japanese under Vice-Admiral Togo had 6 battleships, 8 armoured and 13 light cruisers, several old ships of which 4 could form part of the main fleet, 19 destroyers and 62 sea-going torpedo boats.

Up to 15 May the Japanese were successful in all the operations off Port Arthur, the most effective being mine-laying. The battleship *Petropavlovsk* blew up on a mine and Makarov, the one notable Russian Admiral who had arrived at Port Arthur on 8 March, was lost with her. The battleship *Pobieda* was damaged by a mine, and other Russian losses from various causes were two light cruisers and three destroyers. But on 15 May two Japanese battleships, the *Hatsuse* and *Yashima,* were lost on Russian mines laid the previous afternoon in a dense fog, and the fast light

cruiser *Yoshino* was sunk in collision. From now on the Japanese heavy ships were used as little as possible near Port Arthur, which had been cut off by the Japanese army on land.

On 23 June, when all the damaged battleships had been repaired, the Russian fleet under Rear Admiral Vitgeft left Port Arthur. But on sighting the Japanese that evening, turned back and with torpedo attacks that night achieved nothing. The battleship *Sevastopol* struck a mine and was out of action for six weeks. On 7 August Japanese 4.7inch guns which had been landed began to shell Port Arthur and three days later Vitgeft took his 6 battleships to sea with 4 light cruisers and 8 destroyers under orders from the Tsar to break through to Vladivostock. The battle that ensued is generally known as 'The Yellow Sea'. Altogether 4 battleships, 4 armoured cruisers, 7 light cruisers, 3 old ships, 1 torpedo-gunboat, 17 destroyers and 30 torpedo boats took part on the Japanese side. For a time the Russians fully held their own, but after more than 5 hours a 12inch shell burst on the *Tsessarevitch's* foremast, killing Vitgeft, and a few minutes later another hit the sighting slit on her CT and jammed the helm hard over, so that the Russian line was thrown into confusion. In the next hour and a half the Japanese inflicted much non-fatal damage, but once again the night torpedo attacks failed, though the battleship *Poltava* was hit by a torpedo that did not explode. This ship, with the battleships *Retvisan, Pobieda, Peresviet, Sevastopol,* the cruiser *Pallada* and three destroyers returned to Port Arthur, while the *Tsessarevitch* and the rest made for various neutral ports where they were interned, except for one destroyer that was driven ashore, and the fast light cruiser *Novik* that made for Vladivostok but was disposed of by two Japanese cruisers in the Soya Straits.

Meanwhile, the three Vladivostok armoured cruisers had come south to meet Vitgeft if he succeeded in breaking out and on 14 August they

1

were engaged off Ulsan by four armoured and two light cruisers under Vice-Admiral Kamimura. The oldest of the Russians the *Rurik,* was sunk and the other two got away, though they took no more part in the war.

The Port Arthur fleet did not sortie again, though the *Sevastopol* came out on 23 August and was damaged by a mine. By 1 October the Japanese had emplaced six 11inch howitzers of French pattern and a further 12 were added during the month. It was not, however, until 5 December, when an observation post was established on 203 Metre Hill that the ships could be disposed of. The *Poltava, Retvisan, Peresviet, Pobieda, Pallada,* and the armoured cruiser *Baryan* that had missed the Yellow Sea battle through mine damage, were sunk in succession by the evening of 8 December, while the *Sevastopol* anchored out of sight beyond the harbour entrance. She was protected by a boom and nets and although 123 torpedoes were fired at her, only one hit, though a number exploded in the nets and

caused some damage. The *Sevastopol* was towed into deep water and scuttled at the surrender of Port Arthur on 2 January 1905. The only important Japanese ship lost in this period of the war was the fast light cruiser *Takasago* mined during 12/13 December.

The major part of the Russian battle Fleet left Libau on 15 October 1904 for the Far East. This was already too late, but two of the most powerful ships had only just been completed. Various reinforcements were subsequently sent, the last on 15 February after Port Arthur had fallen, when the expedition should have been called off.

The whole force finally assembled at Van Phong Bay on the coast of French Indo-China on 9 May 1905. It is outside the scope of this feature to relate the story of the voyage of the various Russian squadrons, but it must be said that, without the use of neutral French harbours, particularly in Madagascar where the main part of the Baltic fleet stayed for eleven weeks, and also without the collier

service chartered from the Hamburg Amerika Company, the Russian force would never have reached the war area. In point of fact the long stay at Madagascar was due to difficulties over the supply of coal and the need to re-negotiate the charter.

The force which left Indo-China comprised 8 battleships, 3 coast-defence ships, 3 old armoured cruisers, 5 light cruisers, 5 auxiliary cruisers (ex-liners), 1 armed yacht, 9 destroyers and a fleet train of 1 repair ship, 2 armed transports, 9 Russian merchant ships, 2 tugs and 2 hospital ships. Among the auxiliary ships which had been intended to accompany the fleet but were prevented by machinery troubles when still in the Baltic, it is of interest to note an ex-liner converted to a balloon ship and the large ice-breaker *Ermak.* The fleet was under the command of Vice-Admiral Rozhestvenski, who seems to have been of no outstanding ability. His main idea was to get to Vladivostok, if possible without a fight, and his battle orders envisaged the use of his cruisers to

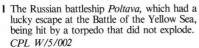

1 The Russian battleship *Poltava,* which had a lucky escape at the Battle of the Yellow Sea, being hit by a torpedo that did not explode.
CPL W/5/002

2 The Japanese cruiser *Hatsuse,* sunk by a mine on 15 May 1904.
Marius Bar

3 The Japanese light cruiser *Yoshino,* the victim of a collision early in the war.
National Maritime Museum

4 The battleship *Petropavlosk,* whose loss to a mine deprived Russia of the services of the distinguished Admiral Makarov, who was killed when she sank.
CPL W/5/003

5 The battleship *Pobieda* was in action at the Yellow Sea and was later sunk at Port Arthur.
CPL W/5/004

protect the fleet train, his destroyers acting as tenders to the battleships. On the way north 8 of the merchant ships were sent back and 4 of the armed liners were detached to make demonstrations which were quite ineffectual, but the remainder of the fleet train closely accompanied the warships to the end. The Russian battle-line consisted of 12 ships as follows:—

1st Division:
Kniaz Suvarov (Vice-Admiral Rozhestvenski); *Imperator Alexander III; Borodino; Orel;*

2nd Division:
Osliabia (Rear Admiral Felkerzam); *Sissoi Veliki; Navarin; Admiral Nakhimov;*

3rd Division:
Imperator Nikolai I (Rear Admiral Nebogatov); *General-Admiral Graf Apraxin; Admiral Seniavin; Admiral Ushakov.*

THE RUSSIAN SHIPS
The first four ships had been laid down at the St. Petersburg yards in 1899-1901 but not completed until late 1903-1904 and they were not then entirely ready for service. They were high-sided with considerable 'tumblehome' and a nominal displacement of 13 516 tons which was well exceeded. There were four 12inch twin electrically trained French-type turrets fore and aft, and twelve 6inch twin turrets of similar type, three on either beam.

Some of the Russian reinforcements for the Pacific. From left to right: two *Orel* class battleships, the *Sissoi Veliki, Svietlana* and *Almag.*
CPL W/5/005

Twelve of the twenty 3inch were in a main deck battery and the rest in bow and stern casemates. The heavy armour was KC made in Russia or America, with some from Britain. There was a complete belt 11 ft wide and $7\frac{1}{2}$-6 in amidships reduced to $5\frac{3}{4}$-4 in at the ends. The main deck battery was protected by 3 inch armour, and the 12 in turrets had 10 in with $2\frac{1}{2}$ in roofs and 9-7 in bases reduced to 4 in behind the belt. The secondary turrets and bases had 6 in armour with $1\frac{3}{4}$-4 in roofs and the CT 8 in with a 5 in tube. The main deck was 2 in with a 1 in lower deck ($1\frac{1}{4}$ in slopes) and the upper deck over the 3 in battery $2\frac{1}{2}$-$1\frac{1}{2}$ in. There was a $1\frac{1}{4}$ in torpedo bulkhead at a maximum of 6ft 8in inboard. Twenty Belleville boilers in two boiler rooms and two sets of engines gave 16 000 ihp for about $17\frac{1}{2}$ knots.

The *Osliabia,* sister to the *Peresviet* of the Port Arthur fleet, was a thoroughly bad design, built at St Petersburg in 1895-1901. She was also high-sided with a nominal displacement of 12 674 tons and a beam of only $71\frac{1}{2}$ ft. The main armament was only four 10inch twin French-type turrets fore and aft, with eleven 6inch of which one was unprotected in the bows, six in upper deck and four in main deck casemates. Of the twenty 3inch guns, eight were in an unprotected main deck battery. The heavy armour was mainly American Harvey with some KC. Of the $426\frac{1}{2}$ ft waterline, 312 ft was protected by a belt 7 ft 10 in wide and 9 in amidships (5 in lower edge) but reduced to 7 in fore and aft where

there were 4 in bulkheads. Above the belt was 188 ft of 5 in armour to the main deck ending in 4 in bulkheads reaching to the forecastle deck. All the 4 in bulkheads had unarmoured doors. The turrets were 9 in with 5 in bases, the casemates 5 in and the CT 6 in. There was a $2\frac{1}{2}$ in lower armoured deck extending to bow and stern with 3 in slopes, but none of the other decks were over $\frac{1}{2}$ in. Thirty two Belleville boilers in four rooms with three sets of engines gave a designed 14 500 ihp = 18 knots.

The *Sissol Veliki* built in 1892-1896 had a normal displacement of 10 400 tons. There were four 12inch fore-and-aft twin French type turrets, and six 6inch in a main deck battery. The armour was Nickel steel, not Harveyised, with an incomplete belt 16-12 in (4 in lower edge) ending in 9 in bulkheads. The deck was $1\frac{3}{4}$ in over the belt and 3 in below water outside the bulkheads. The armour above the belt was 5 in to the main deck with the same on the battery. The turrets and bases had 12 in armour. Speed was 15.7 knots originally.

The *Navarin* built in 1889-1896 was a low freeboard turret ship of 10 200 tons normal displacement resembling a smaller *Nile* and *Trafalgar.* There were four 12inch fore-and-aft twin turrets, with all-round loading but without individual armour to the turret bases, and eight 6inch on the upper deck. The belt of compound armour was 16-14 in (8 in lower edge) ending in 12 in bulkheads. Above this was a shorter 12 in

upper belt, while the deck was 3 in beyond the belt, $2\frac{1}{2}$ in over the belt outside the upper belt, and 2 in over the latter. The battery had 5 in and the turrets 12 in Nickel steel, not Harveyised. The original speed was about $15\frac{1}{2}$ knots.

The *Nikolai* built in 1885-1891 resembled the British *Sans Pareil* in general layout but had a short higher forecastle. Of 9672 tons displacement, she carried two 12inch in a turret forward, while on the main deck were four 9inch with some protection and eight 6inch with none. There was a complete waterline belt, 14 in max. with 10 in on the turret, the armour being compound. Speed was at most 15 knots originally.

The *Nakhimov* was an old armoured cruiser, launched in 1885 and reconstructed. Of 8500 tons, her armament comprised eight 8inch in fore and aft and beam twin barbettes with ten 6inch. There was a short waterline compound belt of 10-6 in and 8-7 in on the barbettes with a 3 in deck at the belt upper edge amidships and below the waterline at the ends. The original speed had been 17 knots but was only 14 knots in 1904. The *Apraxin, Seniavin* and *Ushakov* were small coast defence ships launched in 1893-96. Their nominal displacement was 4126 tons and the armament four 10inch, (three only in *Apraxin*) in fore-and-aft turrets, with in addition four 4.7inch QF. The 10inch guns were a lower velocity model than those in the *Osliabia*. The thicker armour was Harvey with a partial belt on the waterline of 10 in max. and 8 in on

the turrets, with 2-3 in on the armour deck. Trial speeds were about 16 knots.

The first seven battleships were the only vessels really fit for the battle-line, and of these the *Navarin* had older pattern 12inch guns of low muzzle-velocity. Of the four ships of the *Borodino* class, three had only completed shortly before the first part of the Fleet left Russia, and their trials had been hurried; troubles with the steering occurred on the voyage. A large proportion of the Russian crews was inadequately trained, while the second-in-command, Felkerzam, was in poor health and died four days before the battle with the Japanese was fought. His flag-captain was ordered to lead his division, while Nebogatov, whose ships had been the last to reach Indo-China, never discussed the battle plans with Rozhestvenski.

The cruisers comprised the *Oleg* (Rear Admiral Enkvist), a new 23-knot ship with twelve 6inch guns; the *Aurora,* 20 knots and eight 6inch guns, sister to the *Pallada* of the Port Arthur fleet; the *Svietlana,* 20 knots and six 6inch guns and the *Jemtchug* and *Izumrud,* six 4.7inch guns and of 23-24 knots speed. In addition there were two reconstructed armoured cruisers older than the *Nakhimov,* the *Vladimir Monomakh* and *Dmitri Donskoi,* both with 6inch and 4.7inch guns and a speed of perhaps 15 knots. The armed yacht *Almaz* and the armed liner *Ural,* could make 19 and 20 knots speed but were only lightly gunned. The train limited the fleet speed to 9

knots, but the warships could not have maintained a much higher speed as the *Nikolai,* which was heavily loaded and very foul, had a maximum speed of only 12 knots, and the three ships of the *Ushakov* class were hardly any faster.

Rozhestvenski decided on the most direct route to Vladivostok through the Straits of Korea, and after passing to the north of Luzon and to the east of Formosa, entered the East China Sea. He intended to pass through the eastern half of the Straits of Korea, between the Island of Tsushima and Japan at midday on 27 May, and coaled for the last time on 23 May at sea. It is usually said that the amount of coal taken on was regulated to give the Russian ships their normal load by noon of 26 May, when a battle was expected, but the three small ships of the *Ushakov* type appear to have had a good deal more than their designed quantity. Further reference is made to this point when discussing the fate of the *Borodino* class.

The Russian ships already at Vladivostok took no part in the forthcoming operations. The Japanese had laid extensive minefields off Vladivostok and the large armoured cruiser *Gromoboi* had been seriously damaged by a mine on 23 May. The light cruiser *Bogatyr,* sister to the *Oleg,* had been very badly injured by running ashore in the earlier part of the war and her repair was beyond the resources of Vladivostok. This left only the large armoured cruiser *Rossiya* and some torpedo boats, and they remained inert.

4

1

2

ГРОМОБОЙ
Gromoboi

3

5

1 The fast light cruiser *Novik* which escaped after the battle of the Yellow Sea. While making for Vladivostok, she was intercepted by two Japanese cruisers and sunk in the Soya Straits.
CPL W/5/008

2 The battleship *Sissoi Veliki,* part of the Second Division of Roghestvenski's fleet, was a 10 400 ton vessel completed in 1896.
CPL W/5/009

3 *Navarin* was completed in the same year but construction had commenced as early as 1889. *CPL W/5/010*

4 The battleship *Sevastapol* played an eventful, if ill-fated, part in the war: she struck a mine on 23 June 1904, resulting in a 6 week repair; this was completed just in time for her to sail with the Russian fleet to its defeat at the Yellow Sea. *CPL W/5/011*

5 The armoured cruiser *Gromoboi* was severely damaged by mines off Vladivostock and spent the whole of the war inactive in that port. *CPL W/5/012*

1 The Japanese battleship *Asahi* at Southampton in 1899.
CPL W/5/006

2 The Italian built armoured cruiser *Nisshin* at Port Said in October 1917.
Imperial War Museum

2

THE JAPANESE SHIPS

The Japanese fleet, the ships of which had been given essential refits since the fall of Port Arthur, was concentrated in the Straits of Korea. The heavy ships were based at Masanpo in southern Korea, while some of the light cruisers and torpedo-craft were at Osaki Bay and Takeshiki in Tsushima. A watch on the Straits of Korea was maintained by light cruisers reinforced by armed merchant ships and old warships.

The Japanese battle-line, like the Russian, consisted of twelve ships. These were organised in two divisions which were to act together or independently as circumstances indicated. The first comprised the four battleships with two armoured cruisers, and the second six armoured cruisers. The order was as follows:-

1st Division:
Mikasa (Admiral Togo);
Shikishima; Fuji; Asahi; Kasuga;
Nisshin (Vice-Admiral Misu).

2nd Division:

Izumo (Vice-Admiral Kamimura); *Azuma; Tokiwa; Yakumo; Asama; Iwate* (Rear Admiral Shimamura).

The *Mikasa* had been built by Vickers in 1898-1902 and had an actual normal displacement of 14 358 tons. She had four 12inch guns in fore-and-aft twin turrets, the mountings by Elswick generally resembling the British BVI in HMS *Formidable.* There were fourteen 6inch, ten in a main deck battery and four in upper deck casemates, and twenty 3inch. The heavy armour was largely KC with a nearly complete belt 7 ft 8 in wide ending in a stern 6 in bulkhead. It was 9 in for 158 ft amidships, thinning to 7 in by the barbette bases, at the outside of which were shallow 12 in bulkheads, and beyond these the belt reduced to $5\frac{1}{2}$ in and 4 in. The upper belt and battery armour extended for 158 ft and was 6 in with angled 6 in bulkheads to the inner sides of the barbettes. The battery had 2 in screens and 1 in longitudinal bulkheads, and the four casemates were 6 in with 2 in rear walls. The turrets were 10-8 in with 3 in roofs and the barbettes and CT 14 in, the former reduced to 10 in behind the 6 in bulkheads. The armour deck was 2 in amidships with 3 in slopes and 2 in at the ends, but by the barbettes in the space between the lines of the 12 in and 6 in bulkheads, it was curved and $4\frac{1}{2}$ in thick ($1\frac{1}{2}$ in nickel steel on 3 in mild steel). There was also a 1 in upper deck over the battery. The 25 Belleville boilers and two sets of engines gave 16 430 ihp = 18.5 knots on trials.

The *Shikishima* and *Asahi* built by Thames Ironworks and Clydebank in 1897-1900 differed in details from each other, and in appearance, being respectively three and two funnelled. Actual normal displacements were 14 431 and 14 525 tons. The armament was as in the *Mikasa,* except that the 12 in mountings resembled the British BIV in HMS *Glory,* and that the 6inch guns were in eight main deck and six upper deck casemates. The heavy armour was Harvey-nickel, and the 9 in belt extended for 220

ft (224 ft in *Asahi*) and was 8 ft 2 in wide (8 ft in *Asahi*). Shallow-angled 12 in bulkheads ran to the barbettes, and beyond these the belt was reduced to 7 in, $5\frac{1}{2}$ in, 4 in, extending to stem and stern. The upper belt reached to the main deck and was 6 in with 6 in bulkheads. The turrets were 10-8 in and the barbettes 14 in reduced to 10 in behind the 6 in armour. The casemates were 6 in with 2 in rear walls and the CT 14 in. The armour deck was $2\frac{1}{2}$ in with 4 in slopes amidships, and the main deck was 1 in here. With machinery generally similar to that of the *Mikasa,* trials gave *Shikishima* 15 355 ihp = 18.6 knots, *Asahi* 15 593 ihp = 18.3 knots.

The *Fuji,* built by Thames Ironworks in 1894-1897, was of an older type of 12 450 tlons normal displacement. Four 12inch guns were in twin fore-and-aft shielded barbettes with end-on main and all-round auxiliary loading, the mountings resembling the British BII in HMS *Prince George.* There were ten 6inch guns, four in main deck casemates and six in shields on the upper deck. The heavy armour was Harvey with a 226 ft x 8 ft belt, 18 in amidships (8 in lower edge) reduced to 14 in by the barbettes and ending in 14-12 in bulkheads. Above this was 4 in armour to the main deck with 6 in bulkheads, while the casemates were 6 in (2 in rear walls). The pear-shaped barbettes were 14 in, reduced to 9-4 in behind the 4 in side, with 6-4 in shields to the 12inch guns. The CT was 14 in and the armour deck $2\frac{1}{2}$ in at the main belt upper edge amidships and below the waterline at the ends. Ten cylindrical boilers and two sets of engines gave a forced draught 14 100 ihp = 18.5 knots on trials, but this was much reduced by the time of Tsushima.

Of the armoured cruisers, the *Kasuga* and *Nisshin* had been built by Ansaldo in 1902-1904 and bought by Japan from Argentina. They were of the *Garibaldi* type, displacing about 7700 tons normal. They differed in armament, the

Kasuga having one 10inch forward and a twin 8inch turret aft while the *Nisshin* had twin 8inch fore-and-aft. Both had fourteen 6inch, ten in a main deck battery and four in upper deck shields, as well as ten 3inch. The armour was Terni Harvey-nickel with a complete belt about 10 ft wide. This was 6 in amidships with $4\frac{3}{4}$ in bulkheads, and continued to the ends at $4\frac{1}{2}$ in, $3\frac{1}{2}$ in and 3 in. Above this was 170 ft of 6 in armour to the upper deck, ending in $4\frac{3}{4}$ in bulkheads. The main armament had 6-4 in, the CT 6 in, and the armour deck was 1 in with $1\frac{1}{2}$ in slopes. The upper deck was $1\frac{1}{2}$ in over the 170 ft of citadel armour, and beyond this there was $\frac{3}{4}$ in at the belt upper edge. They had cylindrical boilers, speed was a bare twenty knots and the *Nisshin* in particular had a very large turning circle.

The other six armoured cruisers generally resembled each other. The *Azuma* was built at St. Nazaire, the *Yakumo* by Vulcan, Stettin, and the other four by Elswick, the dates being 1898 to 1901, except for the *Asama* and *Tokiwa* in 1896-1899. Normal displacement was 9300-9750 tons, and all had four 8inch, in fore-and-aft twin turrets. The Elswick ships had fourteen 6inch in six main deck and four upper casemates, and four upper deck shields, while the other two had twelve 6inch, two main deck casemates being absent; all had twelve 3inch. The armour was Harvey or Harvey-nickel in the Elswick ships and KC in the other two. The detailed distribution varied, but in general all had a belt about 7 ft wide, 7 in amidships and 4-3 in at the ends, rising to the main deck at the bow. The upper belt amidships was 5 in, with 6 in on turrets, and casemates and 14-12 in on the CT. The armour deck was 2 in or $2\frac{1}{2}$ in. The *Asama* and *Tokiwa* had cylindrical boilers and the others Belleville. Speeds were 20-21 knots, the *Azuma* being the slowest, and the *Tokiwa* with a trials speed of 22.73 knots originally, the fastest.

The Japanese had twelve light cruisers as well as the three *Matsushima's* (one 12.6 in, eleven

ADZUMA   ADZUMA   JAPANESE.

1

2

1 The French built armoured cruiser *Azuma*.
CPL W/5/007

2 The Japanese cruiser *Chitose*.
Imperial War Museum

or twelve 4.7 in, 16 knots) and the old battleship *Chin Yen* (four short 12 in, four 6 in, originally 14½ knots), and three torpedo gunboats which served as despatch vessels. They also had 21 destroyers and, including local flotillas, 44 torpedo boats, armed respectively with 18 in and 14 in torpedoes having explosive charges of up to 220 and 132 lb.

One of the destroyer divisions was also equipped with mines, and it appears that other torpedo craft would have been used for mining, forming a special detachment under the *Asama*, but this plan was cancelled due to the bad weather. Apart from the *Kasagi* and *Chitose* (4900 and 4760 tons respective normal displacements, two 8inch,

ten 4.7inch, 22½ knots), the light cruisers were of 2450 to 3700 tons, with 6inch and 4.7inch guns and original trial speeds of 18 to 21 knots.

The battle which was fought between these fleets on 27 and 28 May, 1905 is usually known as the Battle of Tsushima, though Togo in his official report, called it the Battle of the Japan Sea. It resulted in the annihilation of the Russian fleet at very small cost to the Japanese. Their war-experienced officers and men were greatly superior to the Russians and Admiral Togo was much the better commander. The Japanese ships in the line of battle were generally better than the Russians and they could maintain a speed of 15 knots,

with a possible 17-18 knots for the 2nd Division, as against a Russian figure of 11-12 knots. On the other hand there were only four Japanese battleships as against seven Russian (excluding the *Nikolai*), and the Japanese had only sixteen 12inch and one 10inch compared with twenty 12inch, six older 12inch and fifteen 10inch guns. Their superiority in 6inch guns was not likely to be important but they had thirty 8inch as against two 9inch and six 8inch of older models on the broadside. With the earlier battles of the war in mind, there was little reason to expect such a complete victory, the relative ease of which was not anticipated by the Japanese.

GUNS IN RUSSIAN LINE OF BATTLE

GUN	Weight (tons)	Bore (cals)	Shells (lb)	MV (fs)	Notes
12inch Obukhov/Canet	42.0-42.7	38.3-38.4	729	2600	*Borodino* class; *Sissoi*
12inch Obukhov/Krupp	55.2	31.9	729	2090	*Navarin*
12inch Obukhov/Krupp	50.6	27	729	1870	*Nikolai*
10inch Obukhov/Canet	27	43.3	496	2550	*Osliabia*
10inch Obukhov/Canet	22.1-22.6	43.5	496	2275	*Apraxin, Ushakov* class
9inch Obukhov/Krupp	21.7	32	277	2325	*Nikolai*
8inch Obukhov/Krupp	13.5	32	193	2300	*Nakhimov*
6inch Obukhov/Canet	5.7	43.5	91	2600	*Borodino* class; *Osliabia, Sissoi*
6inch Obukhov/Brinke	6.3	33.5	91	2300	*Navarin, Nikolai, Nakhimov*
6inch Obukhov wire	5.0				
4.7inch/(120mm) Obukhov/Canet	2.9	43.5	45	2700	*Aprakin, Ushakov* class
3inch/(75mm) Obukhov/Canet	0.9	48.2	10.8	2700	*Borodino* class; *Osliabia*

IN JAPANESE LINE OF BATTLE

12inch Elswick Patterns G,G[1]	48.5-48.9	40.4	850	2400	All four battleships
10inch Elswick Pattern R	30.9	40.35	500	2297	*Kasuga*
8inch Elswick Patterns S,U,W	18.5-19.1	45	250	2480	All eight armoured cruisers
6inch Elswick Pattern various	5.8-6.6	40	100	2300	All battleships and armoured cruisers
3inch Elswick Pattern N	0.6	40	12.5	2210	All but *Fuji*

Note: The Japanese had a considerable reserve of 12inch, as they had purchased 20 spare guns.

THE
Salt Lake City
CLASS
by Norman Friedman

Most accounts of the 'Treaty' cruisers suggest that the 10000 ton/8inch gun limit imposed at Washington in 1922 was inspired entirely by the characteristics of the new British *Hawkins* class cruisers, which mounted 7.5inch main batteries. The reality, at least in the US case, was rather more complex. American interest in really large cruisers dates from the post-World War I shift from European to Pacific considerations. From 1919 on the most probable enemy was Japan, and the most probable war scenario was a fleet advance across the Pacific towards a decisive battle in Japanese home waters and to accomplish the relief of the Philippines.

At the same time the US concept of cruiser-functions began to shift. Previous cruisers, which had been designated Scouts *(Omahas)* had been intended largely for operations in direct support of the Battle Fleet. However, Pacific warfare would require 'strategic' (as opposed to 'tactical') scouting: reconnaissance on the far side of the Pacific. It

would also require considerable operations on the long trade-routes. At the same time it began to appear that aircraft might well take over most of the fleet scouting function. At a General Board hearing in 1921 one Admiral suggested that the vital cruiser-functions of the future would be:

1 convoy escort against surface raiders.
2 bombardment of lesser enemy bases.
3 driving the enemy's light craft from the sea.

All would require great range and seakeeping ability, ie substantial size.

The question of the 8inch gun was complex. In 1919 the ten light cruisers under construction were to be armed with a high-velocity 6inch/53cal, which would fire the largest shell a man could handle. Indeed, manhandling and individual (broadside) disposition were considered keys to their high rate of fire. The Bureau of Ordnance was interested in a new 8inch/50cal, for future cruisers, but this weapon

could not be loaded by hand and would probably require a turret-mounting. Both power-loading and a multiple mounting were considered very detrimental to a high rate of fire. For example, earlier 8inch/45cal guns mounted in armored cruisers could fire no faster than 12inch turret guns.

Thus a recurrent issue was the 'smothering' effect of rapid 6inch fire versus the smashing effect of individual 8inch hits. Although the 8inch could outrange the smaller gun, it could be argued that its rate of fire would be so slow that few hits would be registered against a rapidly manoeuvering cruiser trying to close the range. In fact hits at very long range would require the complexity of director-control, which in any case would further reduce the rate of fire.

Nor was the evidence from abroad ambiguous. It was true that Britain had built a class of very large cruisers armed with 7.5inch guns, but it could be argued that they had not been particularly successful. Evidence in this direction

Pensacola as refitted at Mare Island, May-June 1945. Note her resemblance to the refitted *Northampton* and *Portland* classes. The large directors are Mk 33s controlling the 5inch secondary battery; superimposed above them are a pair of Mk 35s originally manufactured for the 1850 ton 'leaders', with their single-purpose main batteries. They were later modified for 8inch ballistics, as here. Both sets of directors employed the small Mk 28 force control radar. At this time *Pensacola* mounted seven quadruple Bofors, as well as eleven twin 20mm machine guns. Her foremast shows SK air search and SG surface search radar; smoke obscures the SP fighter control set on her mainmast, but the array of jamming gear is visible.

1 The *Salt Lake City* in dockyard hands, May 1943.
USN

Midships and after superstructure, *Salt Lake City,* May 1943.
USN

Salt Lake City was scheduled for an overhaul similar to *Pensacola*'s, but never received one. Here she is in June, 1944, showing her original very tall foremast with its Mk 22 8inch director (Mk 3 radar); the 5inch director carries the Mk 4 radar system. Her 40mm battery corresponded to that of her sister ship except for the bow mount, which she lacked.

included the completion of one such ship, *Vindictive* as an aircraft carrier, and the evident decision to retreat to more moderate dimensions and 6inch guns in the succeeding 'E' class. Moreover, there were many reports of British dissatisfaction at the cost of the big cruisers, in manpower as well as money. The Royal Navy decision to assign one to the China station was taken as proof that they were not well-liked in the Fleet. It could also be claimed that no foreign power had gone beyond the 6inch gun, although there was one report that Japan was building a 7800 ton cruiser (which, unknown to the US Navy in 1921, would mount 8inch guns) the *Furutaka*.

These issues were resolved in the usual tortuous manner. Postwar Scout design began early in 1919, with priorities essentially unchanged from those which had produced the *Omahas*. The latter were seen as too large for their firepower, which at the time was limited to eight 6inch/53cal, all mounted on the broadside. Thus in February the Preliminary Design section of the Bureau of Construction and Repair (C & R) began a set of sketch designs in two series:

1 Series A, armed as the *Omahas,* but with displacement decreased as much as possible, speed increased towards 37 knots by using machinery designed for a contemporary Destroyer Leader project. In fact the best that could be done was 36 knots on 6850 tons.

2 Series B, armed with the new 8inch/50cal gun proposed by Ordnance. The initial instruction was to try for four guns, two each fore-and-aft mounted on single turntables with light unarmored enclosures. There were also to be some 5inch rapid-firing guns for protection against destroyers. Quite soon twin 8inch mounts were adopted; a sketch design of March 1919 was presented with the notation that 'this design is believed to be in accordance with the trend of scout or light cruiser design at the present time.' This was an

8100-tonner of 35 knots.

Note that Design B, at least as originally conceived, is not far from that adopted by Japan at this time.

The Scout project was maintained at relatively low priority in view of the large number of *Omahas* not even in service as yet; the preliminary design team was small and the number of tasks large. Work on the Scout lapsed in March and was not resumed until early October. At this time sketch designs were still being prepared largely on the initiative of the designers, *not* on the basis of specific requests from any planning authority (the General Board or perhaps the Office of [the Chief of Naval] operations). In any case, a new series, C, was begun essentially

Official US Navy plans of *Pensacola* in 1941, showing her arrangement prior to war modification. Note her pronounced sheer.

as an answer to the British *Hawkins* class: seven 8inch/50cal in unarmored turrets; four 5inch/51cal anti-destroyer guns; two triple torpedo-tubes; light side armor (2inch STS splinter armor laid over a 1inch side) over the machinery; a speed of 36 knots; and an endurance of 10 000 miles at 10 knots. What was unusual was the arrangement of the battery: a triple mount forward, and two twins (or, for eight guns, one twin and one triple) aft.

However, the preliminary designers were well aware that this large ship did not represent any kind of official policy. They tried, therefore, a series of much smaller unarmored designs: D and E, with five 6inch/53cal and two twin torpedo-tubes, and speeds of 33.5 and 35.25 knots (which cost 5000 and 5750 tons, respectively); and F, 35 knots and six 8inch guns on 6500 tons.

All of these were presented to

Commander Pye, who much later would command the Battle Force in World War II, at the Office of Operations. He appears to have been the first policy planner to have seen the alternative Scout designs, and his view ran contrary to the basic assumptions of the designers. He considered very high speed wasteful (30 knots in a seaway would be enough) and large ships undesirable 'inasmuch as their cost would permit of building not mere than two-thirds of the number of lighter vessels for a given appropriation... further... armor of the thickness practical for scouts was not of sufficient value to warrant the expenditure of the necessary weight. He was very anxious to obtain a large cruising radius...' Of course Pye did not appreciate the fact that large cruising radius and good speed in a seaway — 30 knots would be no mean achievement — in themselves implied considerable size.

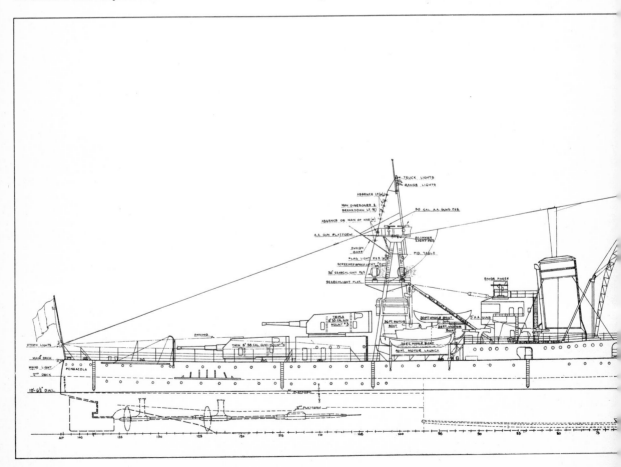

He suggested that Designs D and F be developed, but with reduced speeds. The General Board, responsible for the Characteristics (staff requirements) of new warships, did not share his views, and in March 1920 produced Characteristics calling for deck- and side-armor and for a speed of 35 knots or better. Speed and armor alone would push up displacement, and quite soon a 600 foot hull of about 10 000 tons was now under consideration, for a speed of 35.8 knots, based on Series C.

The General Board's 1920 Characteristics had not produced any ships; in January, 1921 the entire question of Scout armament came up again in the General Board. Admiral Rodgers opened the hearing with a statement that the size of the Pacific Ocean demanded larger ships; and that if the USN wanted to match other navies it would have to go to the 8inch gun. Such ships would be very costly, as the design series had shown: even on 10 000 tons there would be only eight guns and a radius of 8000 nm at 10 knots, where 10 000 would be preferable by far. Moreover, these large ships would have only splinter protection, provided by a 2.5inch deck with 4.5inch slopes and 2.5inch armor at the waterline — and all of that over the machinery only. Magazines would have only deck protection, and turrets and barbettes might well be unarmored. The Bureau of Engineering noted that the full tonnage was required for 35 knots: 'on 7500 it is a tight squeeze to get 32.'

The only question was 6inch vs 8inch guns. Although the 8inch gun could fire to 34 000 yards at 40° elevation, and the 6inch to only about 26 000, it could be argued that few hits would be made outside 24 000, to which a pedestal-(ie broadside)-mounted 6inch could fire (30° elevation). As for penetration, it was true that a 6inch shell could not penetrate a 3inch deck — but neither could an 8inch. It might be true that the heavier shell would behave better at longer ranges, but the lighter one would fire a lot faster, and the Chief of the Bureau of Ordnance went on record as preferring a 6inch cruiser against a *Hawkins*. Commander G J Rowcliff of Ordnance observed:

'It seems to me, Admiral, that in our service the 8inch gun has always been a sort of mongrel type: it is not heavy enough to be effective against an armored ship and has not been light enough to get much rapidity of fire. If we could guarantee for this gun a performance of six to eight shots per minute it might be well to consider it; but I do not believe we can get anything like that, and we believe we can get it from the 6inch gun. It might be different, however, with twin 6inch guns.'

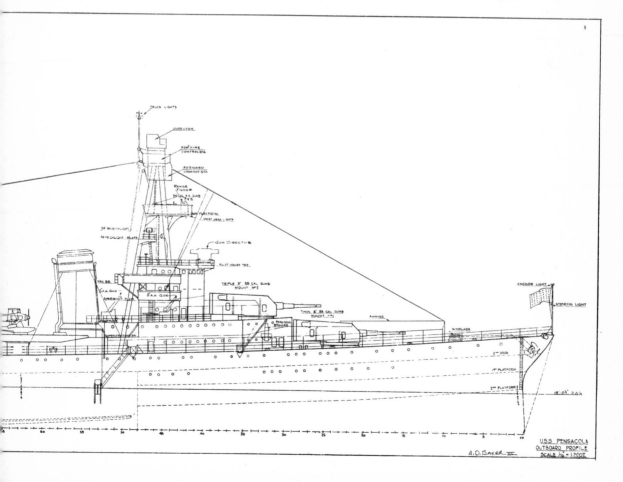

U.S.S. PENSACOLA
OUTBOARD PROFILE
SCALE ⅟₁₆" = 1 FOOT

A.D. BAKER III

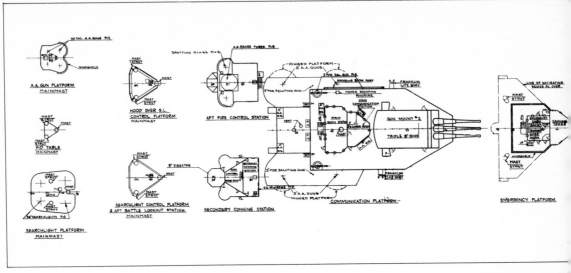

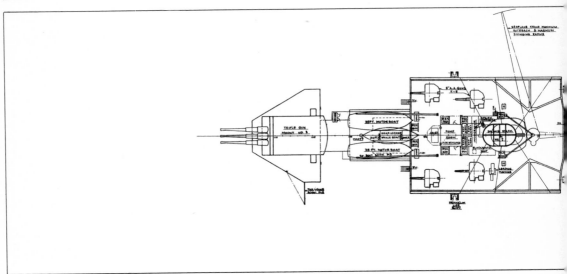

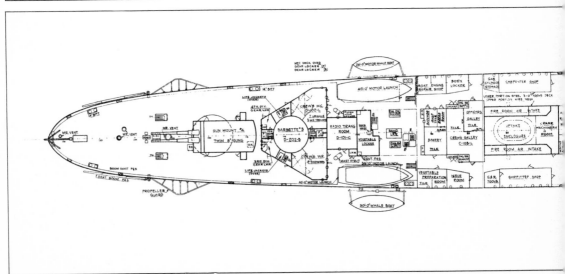

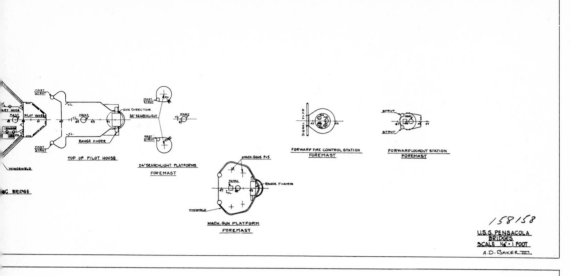

158158

U.S.S. PENSACOLA
BRIDGES
SCALE 1/16" = 1 FOOT
A.D. BAKER III

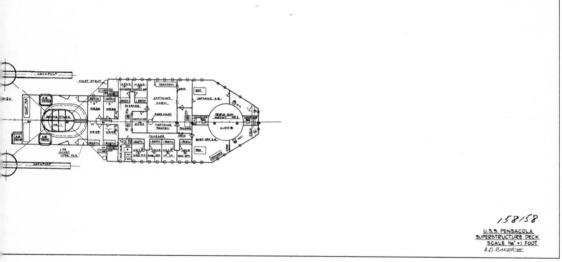

158158

U.S.S. PENSACOLA
SUPERSTRUCTURE DECK
SCALE 1/16" = 1 FOOT
A.D. BAKER III

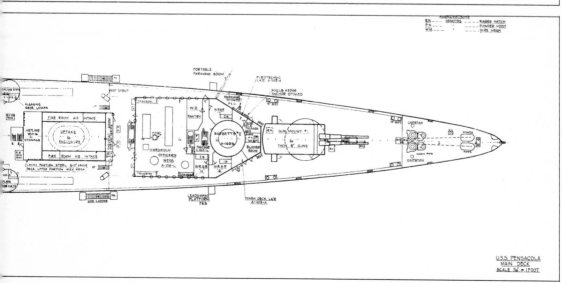

U.S.S. PENSACOLA
MAIN DECK
SCALE 1/16" = 1 FOOT

In fact the multiple 8inch guns were generally rated at three rounds per minute.

It appeared that on 10 000 tons the ordnance weights would suffice for eight 8inch or about 16 6inch; but the Bureau of Ordnance was unhappy with broadside mounts, which it considered uneconomical. That meant multiple 6inch mounts on the centerline, and topweight precluded more than two levels. Hence it seemed in 1921 that any 6inch cruiser would have to have 12 guns in four triple mounts (quadruple mounts were not even considered).

In that case the rates of fire of 6inch and 8inch guns might not be so very different. Both batteries would operate by director control and both would require power operation. Now questions of smashing effect per broadside became important. Eight 8inch guns would deliver about 2000 lb of shell, 12 6inch about 1200 lb. Moreover, both C & R and Ordnance had to admit that on 10 000 tons armor might be provided which could resist 6inch *but not 8inch* fire, in the form of an inclined deck.

These arguments proved decisive, and in April 1921 the General Board proposed new cruiser Characteristics: 8 8inch guns in splinter-proof mountings, 4 5inch/25cal two triple torpedo-tubes, a speed of 34 knots and a radius of action of 10 000 miles at 10 knots. In addition 'without sacrifice of other important features these vessels [are] to be designed to resemble the battlecruiser in silhouette'. Thin armor was envisaged: a 1 inch deck with 1.5 inch slopes, and a 1.5inch belt.

These Characteristics were based on a series of what must have been relatively disappointing design studies. The basic scheme, designated No 1, was progressively modified with reduced speed (a), reduced protection (b), reduced battery (c), and all three reductions (d); and the General Board had to decide that all it could afford was (b):

1 Two views of *Pensacola,* 3 July 1945. This detail view shows clearly the extent to which the forward bridgework was cut down. The jamming gear aft is clearly shown: from the masthead down, the TDY jamming system, SP height-finding radar flanked by IFF antennae; radar intercept and direction finding gear; and, at the base of the mainmast a pair of jammers in large radomes. The ship in the background is the cruiser *Indianapolis* (CA 35), which was lost at the end of July.

2 Note the removal of the starboard catapult, a standard weight-saving measure in US cruisers at the end of World War Two. *Pensacola* and *Salt Lake City* were the only US heavy cruisers without hangars: note the stowage of a spare wing under the port 5inch gun, and of spare wingtip floats (circled) abaft the Mk 51 AA director near the funnel.

Plans and uncredited photos, USN official, by courtesy of A D Baker III

Scheme	l	a	b	c	d
Displacement	12000	10750	10000	11250	8250 tons
Length	635	610	600	625	560 feet
Speed	34.5	*33*	34.5	34.5	*33* knots
Power	125000	96000	118000	122000	88000 shp
8inch guns	8	8	8	*6*	*6*
Deck	3	3	*1*	3	*1* inches
Slopes	4.5	4.5	*1.5*	4.5	*1.5*
Side	5	5	*1.5*	5	*1.5*

In each case radius of action was 8000 nm at 10 knots; reductions are underlined. It was estimated that a 4inch belt and a 2.5 inch deck would provide immunity against 6inch/53cal fire between 11 000 and 21 000 yards; the combination of 5inch belt and 3 inch deck would resist 8inch fire between 16 000 and 21 000 yards. All of these designs incorporated a 1inch STS belt extending from the main belt to the bow, the function of which was to prevent the waterline forward from being torn up by penetrating hits: very serious damage forward would slow the ship so much as to doom her. However, main belt protection was limited to the area over engines and boilers. Placing the magazines below the waterline and below an armored deck was considered adequate protection, and light protection of barbettes and even turrets was considered acceptable.

These, then, were the 10 000-ton/8inch gun cruisers which the United States tried successfully to obtain at the Washington Conference. Of course they were not quite what the United States actually built.

The Washington Treaty presented a new problem in cruiser-design. For the first time ships had to be built within a prescribed tonnage limit. Even worse, the tonnage limit was based, not on the usual displacement which included fuel and feed water, but on a new 'standard' measurement which did not. That meant that existing designs had to be re-scaled to give some idea of what could be achieved. For example, 10 000 tons standard was not very far from a 'normal' displacement of about 12 000.

The usual process of feasibility or preliminary design had to be recast to take account of the weight growth common during detailed design and construction; in the post-Treaty series of studies feasibility was reckoned according to the amount of weight margin separating the estimated weights (hull, fittings, battery, armor, machinery, etc) from the 10 000 ton limit. There was really no experience to go by, which is why the first US Treaty designs were completed well within the 10 000 tons.

There was one other new factor. Since the Treaty established a general ceiling on cruisers, it might well be assumed that all of the major naval powers would build 8inch cruisers. In that case protection might not be very useful if it were protection only against 6inch fire — and it might pay to trade heavier armament and higher speed for it. The first US studies, done early in 1923, examined the possibility of mounting 12 8inch guns on a hull with virtually no protection ($\frac{3}{4}$inch STS over magazines, $1\frac{1}{4}$inch over conning tower and steering gear.) A sketch design for 35 knots on 112 000 SHP was rejected because it allowed for only a 133 ton margin. On the other hand a 34 knot type showing a margin of 278 tons was considered acceptable. Ultimately the standard would be a 300 ton margin — but *Salt Lake City* was completed at 9100 tons, *900* tons within the agreed limit.

By April 1923 the Preliminary Designers were working with alternative batteries of 8, 10, or 12 8inch guns, as a 9 gun three turret arrangement was ruled out from the start. They had concluded that serious protection against 8inch shellfire was impossible 'in view of

the fact that only about 700-900 tons could be reasonably expected under any scheme of Scout Cruiser... having minimum requirements for at least 31 knots and eight 8inch/55cal guns.' This would have meant a $4\frac{3}{4}$inch belt, penetrable at up to 20 000 yards, and a $1\frac{1}{2}$inch deck, penetrable at any range beyond 10 000; there would be no zone of immunity at all. 'Consequently we would not be able to protect between the ranges of 10 000 and 20 000 yards, yet in this range somewhere will be the most probable effective battle range.'

On the other hand, some lesser protection would be worthwhile, against destroyers (5inch/51cal beyond 6000 yards) and 6inch cruisers (6inch/53cal beyond 10 000 yards). It turned out that a 3inch side and $1\frac{1}{2}$inch deck were proof against 5inch shell between 6000 and 15 000 yards and the destroyer would find hitting rather difficult at the latter range and the side would be effective against 6inch shell at 10 000 yards. In a few studies it was shown that protection against 8inch fire would require a reduction in speed to 28 knots, which was entirely unacceptable.

The final design, which became *Salt Lake City* and *Pensacola,* was completed at the end of 1925. It called for 10 8inch guns and a speed of 32.5 knots; the emphasis on independent operations at long range shows in a required endurance of 10 000 nm at 15, rather than 10, knots. Armor was set by the destroyer/light cruiser criterion: a main belt 3inches thick, with a 1inch deck amidships. The magazines forward were covered by 4inch side armor and a 1.5inch deck; aft, by the 1.5inch deck and a 3.5inch internal longitudinal bulkhead.

The United States went on to build 16 more 'Treaty' cruisers, each class in turn showing more attention to protection. Ultimately the *Salt Lake City* and her sister would be condemned as over-gunned, under-protected, and of questionable seakeeping capability in view of their low freeboard. There is no question but that they

were compromises loaded towards firepower, but in view of their evolution it appears that the sacrifices made were greater than need be, largely because of the unknown character of the Treaty environment.

The one great question in their design was the validity of the argument in favor of the 8inch gun. US cruiser-evolution shows greater loyalty to this weapon than can be found in any European navy; sometimes it is suggested that the determining factor was somehow bound up with Pacific conditions, since Japan also believed in the big gun.

It is interesting, therefore, to note that a principal argument in favor of the rapid-fire 8inch gun mounted in the *Des Moines* class at the end of World War II was that it would end the *inferiority* of 8inch cruisers faced by rapidly manoeuvering light craft. The 8inch gun with bag ammunition never did much better than three rounds per gun per minute. However, the new light cruisers of the *Brooklyn* and *Cleveland* types were armed with case ammunition which could be fired much more rapidly, as much as ten rounds per gun per minute. They were turret mounted, but they could deliver the old-fashioned 'smothering' fire. It was enough to make one question the whole logic of heavy cruiser design — enough to make a big light cruiser such as HMS *Belfast* a logical proposition indeed.

SOURCES

Material for this article is taken from the Preliminary Design files in the US National Archives and in the Washington National Records Center; and from the records of the General Board held by the Operational Archives at the Washington Navy Yard. I am grateful to Charles Wiseman of the Naval Ship Engineering Center for arranging access to the files at the Washington National Records Center, and to Dr Dean Allard and Mrs Kathy Lloyd for their assistance at the Operational Archives.

The origins of the magnetic mine

by Tom Burton

During the early stages of World War II the Germans achieved outstanding results from the use of magnetic influence ground mines against Allied and neutral shipping in British coastal waters, employing surface vessels, submarines and aircraft to lay them. This successful exploitation of an apparently new weapon has often led to the belief that the magnetic mine was a German invention, but it was not. The British designed the first magnetic firing circuit and used it in ground mines laid offensively off the Flanders coast in the summer of 1918, while the Germans did not commence work on a magnetic mine until 1932.

By the beginning of 1916 the moored contact mine had assumed a major role in combating the U-boat menace and during that year considerable British effort was devoted to mine design; as a result, in 1917 the Royal Navy was supplied with its first reliable moored mine, the type H2. Concurrently, thought had been given to the use of influence-firing as opposed to contact-firing circuits and to the provision of a ground mine, and by the middle of 1918 a magnetically-fired ground mine, the Sinker Mk 1(M), began to come forward. An acoustic firing circuit for attachment to the H2 mine was also designed but was never used.

The Sinker Mk 1(M) was, in essence, a truncated concrete cone filled with about 1000 lb of crude TNT and designed to detonate when actuated by the magnetic field of a ship. It was carried on a reinforced concrete trolley fitted with four non-magnetic wheels gauged to travel on any standard ship's mine rail. A wire or chain strop normally secured the mine to the trolley, but this was removed prior to laying so that the two parts could separate on falling from the mine rail.

The speed of descent of the mine was limited to a maximum of six feet per second by means of a canvas parachute attached to the lifting eyes on top of the mine; this released itself after about fifteen minutes' submergence, by means of a soluble sol ammoniac plug.

The gimballed firing unit operated on the dip-needle principle, whereby the field of a magnetic body would move the needle to complete the firing circuit through a detonator in the primer, the necessary electrical energy for the latter sequence being derived from two Helleson dry cells.

Safeguards included a manual safety pin to hold the battery switch in the 'off' position, until removed just before laying; and hydrostatically operated double-pole primer and battery switches in the

firing circuit. The latter switches, held by soluble plugs with a life of about 40 minutes, kept the mine 'safe' until it had come to rest on the bottom and had time to settle.

A clock-operated anti-countermining arrangement was fitted to all mines; and the firing unit chamber could be flooded and the mine rendered 'safe' (or possibly exploded) after a chosen time by means of a soluble plug.

The principal dimensions of the Sinker Mk 1(M) were:

Diameter of shell (max) 3 ft 4 in
Height from trolley rollers 3 ft 10 in
Weight of Sinker 1950 lb (approx)
Weight of trolley 300 lb (approx)

The first order for the manufacture of Sinkers Mk 1(M) was for no fewer than 10 000 but it was hoped at the time to use them defensively, eg at the inshore ends of the Folkestone—Gris Nes Barrage, as well as offensively. It was intended to use both destroyers and coastal motor boats (CMBs) for the latter task, whereas almost any minelayer would be suitable for the former.

As it happened, trials to establish that the Sinker could be used successfully and safely against submerged submarines were not satisfactorily completed by the end of hostilities and the idea of using it in a defensive role came to naught. The employment of CMBs was also discarded, but only because there was insufficient time to construct the necessary storage facility at Dunkirk, whence the CMBs operated against enemy traffic on the Belgian coast.

The actual laying of the Sinkers was carried out by destroyer minelayers; the first such operation taking place in the afternoon of 8 August 1918, when HMS *Abdiel, Vanoc, Venturous, Vanquisher, Tarpon* and *Telemachus* of the 20th Flotilla, laid a total of 234 units about eight miles north of Dunkirk. The units were laid in several separate lines, with individual unit spacing of 300 ft, and the minelayers were escorted by a further eight destroyers. There was no enemy interference and the Germans were apparently unaware of what was going on. Two underwater explosions, presumed to

be prematures, were heard at the time of laying and reported by Captain (D) 20. But as he also reported great activity ashore, with the very distinct sounds of heavy guns and exploding bombs, and it was established later that, in fact, there was very little such activity in the military lines at the time, there was more than a suspicion that the two sources of explosion might well have been confused.

The matter was to be starkly clarified on the next occasion of laying the Sinker. This was on 22 August when the *Abdiel, Venturous, Vanquisher, Tarpon* and *Telemachus* laid a total of 198 units in three lines, about 17 miles north of Zeebrugge. The minelayers on this occasion were supported by monitors as well as destroyers, while several aircraft scouted over the flotilla and to the south-eastward to prevent enemy aerial observation. Once again there was no enemy interference but 98 premature explosions were observed by the minelaying flotilla and no fewer than 131 were reported from other sources, many, doubtless, due to counter-mining. This massive failure was most disappointing, particularly in view of the reported success of the first operation, and the design team was thereafter busily employed in seeking the cause of this instability and a cure for it.

One further test field of 40 units was laid by HMS *Meteor* on 6 September, about 21 miles north-west of Ostend; but 13 premature explosions were observed on this occasion, some of them up to two hours after laying.

The basic faults in design were not rectified in time for the Sinker Mk 1(M) to be laid again before the signing of the Armistice in

November 1918. However, it is known to have been supplied to the British Naval Command at Archangel in April 1919, during the operations against the Bolsheviks. No account has been found of the use to which these mines were put; but the German archives contain such a reference which, whether accurate or not, serves to confirm the Germans' long-time ignorance of the existence of the device.

In a lecture delivered in 1938, on the stage of development of modern German mining materials and their future development, Rear Admiral Ramien (OC Mining and Barrage Experimental Command, Kiel) stated:

'It was not until long after the war that we learned from Russian officers, who were on a visit to Schwinemünde, that the English in their post-war operations against the Russians had employed a non-contact mine, on the compass principle, in Lake Ladoga. Thus for the first time our suspicions were confirmed that some of the hitherto unexplained explosions and losses off the coast of Flanders in the last year of the war were due to non-contact ground mines.'

It is of interest to note that the Germans subsequently discovered the principle on which these British mines worked and employed the same method of firing—with refinements—in the development of their World War II magnetic circuits; whereas the British abandoned the dip-needle principle for the coiled rod, which took account of the rate of change in strength of the magnetic field in the vicinity of the mine, as opposed to the increase in strength.

SINKER Mk 1 (M)
KEY TO DIAGRAM, AS SHOWN

1. Brass wire reinforcement to base
2. Body of mine — concrete
3. Brass rings to reinforce body
4. Spiral spring to absorb shock on bottoming
5. Primer tube
6. Primer
7. Detonator adaptor
8. Screwed cap to keep detonator in place
9. Detonator
10. Primer switch
11. Combined nuts and lifting eyes
12. Channel connecting primer tube and firing circuit
13. Flooding attachment
14, 14a. Anti-countermining gear
15. Access dome
16. Top cover casting
17. Battery
18. Firing unit
19. Gimbal ring
20. Firing unit chamber
21. Rubber lining to keep TNT away from concrete
22. Brass stays — rubber covered
23. Charge. 1,000lb crude TNT
24. Securing strop

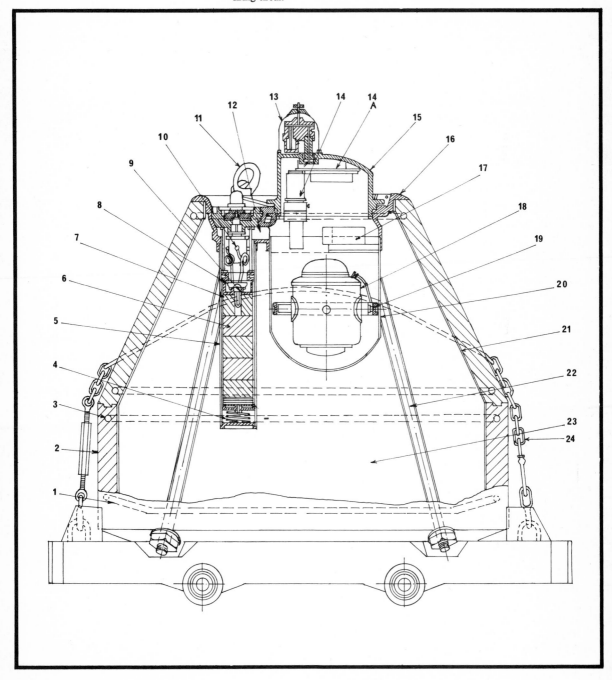

One of the most important parts of the 1936 Naval Treaty was the decision to limit the size of future cruisers to 8000 tons. It was therefore a foregone conclusion that any design of any size would be drawn to that limit. The initial design for the new 8000 ton type were split into two main groups: those with a 6inch main armament, and those with 5.25inch main armament. The 6inch gun designs were produced first, but following the thought that a cruiser with a heavy dual purpose main armament to ward off the increasing threat of air attack was required, a series of alternative schemes were drawn up. Among them was one of 8000 tons with fourteen 5.25inch guns, and a speed of $31\frac{3}{4}$ knots at legend displacement. This particular outline, designated K25G* could well have been chosen to be developed into what was to become the 1937 *Fiji* class programme, had not the argument for the 6inch type prevailed. The drawing shows K25G* as it would have appeared around 1942.

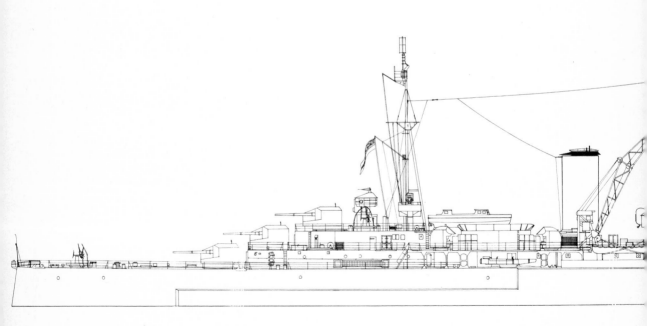

Alan Raven is the co-author of *British Battleships of World War Two* and is currently working on a companion volume on British cruisers.

The 7-Turret Colony class
by Alan Raven

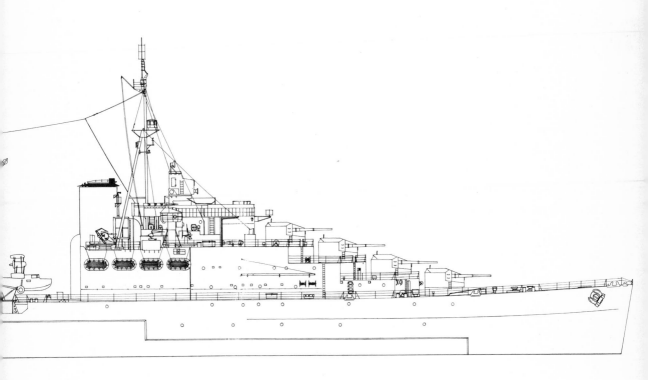

Technical Topics No 4

THE TRANSOM STERN IN THE ROYAL NAVY

By David K Brown

The design of the big battlecruisers of 1920 was severely limited by the number of dry docks which could accept them (see *Warship,* issue 2). Someone at the Admiralty realised that a long, pointed stern, like *Hood's,* only kissed the water and wondered if it would be missed. The Admiralty Experiment Works, Haslar, was asked to test a model of a battlecruiser (43 000 tons, 850 ft length) with the stern cut off in a square transom 30 ft abaft the perpendicular. Further tests were to be made with the transom successively 15 ft and $7\frac{1}{2}$ ft abaft the after perpendicular and finally at the after perpendicular. The resistance of the first three variants was indistinguishable from the original form, only the last extreme cut causing a penalty.

The Superintendent at Haslar (Payne) then indulged in an orgy of cropping; the *Baden, Caradoc* and *Turbinia* models were all given transom sterns. There was a considerable increase in drag for the battleship at all speeds, a slight gain at top speed for the cruiser and a very big gain for *Turbinia.* A transom stern traps a layer of dead water behind it which gives an increased effective length to the ship. Since the economic length for a warship is usually much less than the optimum for hydrodynamic performance at full speed, the transom's gift of effective length without cost is welcome.

Unfortunately, the first large warship built for the Royal Navy after the First World War was the minelayer *Adventure* and the transom stern fitted to her was not a success. Mines dropped into the dead water behind her transom swung back and broke off their horns on her stern, and she had to be rebuilt with a cruiser stern. This made the transom unpopular and it did not reappear until the *Fiji* class cruisers were built.

Transom sterns only reduce the resistance of ships at fairly high speeds where wavemaking drag is important. At lower speeds, resistance will usually increase and a balance has to be struck which depends on the ship's operating pattern. Tests on an aircraft carrier model with a transom area $3\frac{1}{2}$ per cent of the midship area gave the following results:

Speed (kts)	Change in resistance %
30	$4\frac{1}{2}$ reduction
20	4 increase
10	0

For any one speed there will be an optimum size of transom but there is no dramatic change in resistance if this optimum area is slightly exceeded. This is as well since the transom stern has other advantages which often lead the frigate designer into choosing a transom which is bigger than optimum. These are:
1 Increased working area on the quarterdeck
(Particularly useful for helicopter operation)
2 More room for twin rudders and their operating gear
3 Increased buoyancy and waterplane aft which can be useful in designing ships to float after damage
4 Some increase of propulsive efficiency.

On the other hand, all ships get heavier as they grow older and sink deeper into the water. For this reason it is desirable to build a ship with a small transom which will increase through the optimum as the ship grows heavier. As always, the designer must find a happy compromise.

1 The cruiser-minelayer *Adventure,* as completed with the Royal Navy's first transom stern.
CPL W/5/013

Because the transom stern was unsuited to minelaying, it was not employed again until the *Colony* class — clearly demonstrated in this quarter view of *Jamaica* (February 1951).
CPL W/5/014

BOOK REVIEW

Before the Dreadnought — the RN from Nelson to Fisher
by Richard Humble
(Macdonald & Janes)
207pp. 21 illustrations, 4 maps.
£5.95

The very first sentence of this book is encouraging: 'I have always felt that naval historians have been somewhat churlish towards the RN of the 19th century'. Unfortunately Mr Humble is just as churlish towards the warship designer. His book covers life in the Navy, the campaigns of the 19th century after 1815, and developments in ships and guns. For *Warship's* readers this review concentrates on the third section.

Humble asks the question, 'Why did it take so long for new ideas in naval gunnery and warship design to surface?' The best answer was given by Sir Baldwin Walker in 1858, 'It is not in the interest of Great Britain, possessing as she does so large a navy, to adopt any important change in the construction of ships of war which might have the effect of rendering necessary the introduction of a new class of very costly vessels, until such a course is forced upon her by the adoption by foreign powers of formidable ships of a novel character . . .'

This was not 'crusty conservatism' but plain common sense. The Royal Navy's large fleet of conventional ships represented a big investment and it could not afford to render these ships obsolete unnecessarily. The immense industrial power of Great Britain could soon outbuild any

competition, and France's temporary lead in fast wooden battleships with *Le Napoléon* and in armoured ships with *La Gloire* was very soon overtaken by the *Agamemnon* and the *Warrior* respectively. Despite this canny policy the Royal Navy actually led with steamships, iron hulls, screw propellers,[1] steam battleships and turret ships, a record of progress almost ignored by the author. It is time that this simplistic view of a reactionary Admiralty was forgotten.

It is hardly true to say that the last ship built to fight under sail was completed in 1870, as the abandonment of sail was accepted in 1850 and implemented in 1859. Later ships had sails for cruising but fought under steam.

There are a number of minor errors, particularly in the captions to illustrations. On p62 the map dates the Azov expedition as 1854, whereas the text gives it correctly as 1855. The photograph of the *London* following p72 cannot date from 1840; even the RN had not introduced the screw battleship so early!

The statement that for twenty years after 1860 the design of British ironclads dated from before Lissa and Hampton Roads is nonsense. What about *Monarch, Devastation, Inflexible,* not to mention the smaller rams? Was a central battery ship like HMS *Alexandra* identical to the *Warrior* in conception?

HMS *Victory* did not have 64pdr bow chasers (p129); she had 68pdr carronades on the forecastle, but these were close-range weapons, not

chase guns. The 'C' class corvettes (p130) also introduced the armoured deck.

Warrior was not the first ironclad in the RN (p136); that title belongs to the floating batteries of 1855. Having complained of *Inflexible's* brig rig, it is strange that the illustration shows her with the later 'military' rig.

On p139 one could add *Georgia* and *Rappahannock* to the list of Confederate raiders built in Britain. Mention, too, of *Scorpion* and *Wivern* might have been made. The *King Edward VII* (p193) mounted four 9.2inch guns, not eight. The Japanese Kongo (p199) mounted eight, not ten 14inch guns.

This is a readable book, and the accounts of naval actions seem acceptable, making it even more of a pity that the author accepted the conventional view of technical development and selected his facts to fit this theory. A popular book does not require deep scholarship but it can and should avoid bias and factual error. **David K Brown**

---

[1] Seven screw frigates were ordered before the *Alecto* v. *Rattler* trials (see *Warship* No 1).

Warship Photograph Service

As part of the service to readers WARSHIP has come to a special arrangement with the Popperfoto/ Conway Picture Libraries to make available any of their photographs used in the journal. These are credited 'CPL' after the captions and include a reference number for ordering prints. Please note that no other photos from these libraries are available to the general public, and that only two sizes of prints can be supplied.

This offer stands until further notice, although this advertisement may not appear in every issue.

RATES (per print, post free)

		UK	plus 8% VAT
A. Full plate, 6″ x 8″ (162 x 203mm)		£0.50p	4p
B. Continental postcard, 4″ x 6″ (102 x 162mm)		£0.12p	1p

OVERSEAS RATES (VAT does not apply, includes airmail postage to Europe or airmail printed paper rate elsewhere)

	US & Canada	Australia & NZ	Germany	France
A.	$2.00	$1.65	DM3.50	Fr 15
B.	$0.50	$0.45	DM1.00	Fr 4
	Other rates on application			

ORDERING

When ordering please quote your name and address in block capitals, the number, size (**A** or **B**), and reference numbers of the prints required. Payment by cheque, postal or International Money Order, crossed and made payable to Conway Maritime Press Ltd, and endorsed 'A/C Payee'.

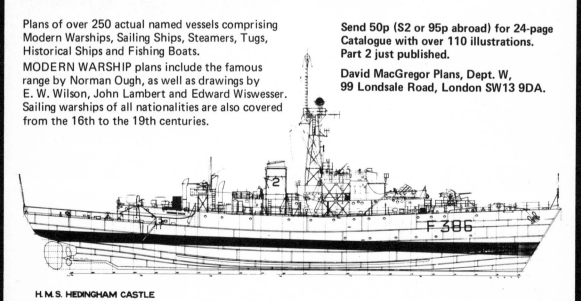